Books by
CLAIRE LEE PURDY

GILBERT AND SULLIVAN
Masters of Mirth and Melody

VICTOR HERBERT
American Music-Master

STORMY VICTORY
The Story of Tchaikovsky

SONG OF THE NORTH
The Story of Edvard Grieg

HE HEARD AMERICA SING
The Story of Stephen Foster

Co-author of
MY BROTHER WAS MOZART

GILBERT & SULLIVAN

Masters of Mirth and Melody

GILBERT and
Masters of Mirth

By
CLAIRE LEE PURDY

Julian Messner, Inc.

SULLIVAN
and Melody

Illustrated by
ERIC GODAL

New York

GILBERT & SULLIVAN

Masters of Mirth and Melody

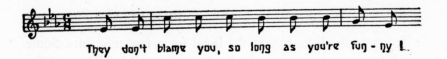

They don't blame you, so long as you're fun-ny L.

GALLANTLY saluting the trim English nurse-maid, two pleasant Italian men stopped to speak to her and her little charge, a handsome boy of two years. The men spoke fluent English, with just enough accent to make their speech fascinating to a naïve servant girl who had never before traveled on the Continent.

"Good morning!" They smiled at the flustered girl, and rolled dark eyes in a way that made her heart beat outrageously.

"And good morning to you, William! Or should we call you by your pet name *Bab?*"

William looked up trustingly, quite at ease with the genial strangers.

The maid had never seen the two men before, but the friendliness and charm of their manner disarmed her. The very fact that they knew little William's nickname convinced her that they must be good friends of her employers, the William Gilberts, who were making a vacation stay in the town of Naples. She was not surprised or suspicious when one of the men remarked, "Mr. Gilbert asked us to tell you, if we happened to meet, that his

I

wife wants the little boy at the hotel for a few moments. Some English friends have arrived who want to see Bab." Then as if a sudden thought had struck him, he added, "But you are having a pleasant stroll, and it's such a lovely morning. Let us take him back to the hotel. We are on our way to breakfast there."

It was all very convincing and pleasant. The maid gladly gave the boy into the keeping of the strangers.

After she had walked a while in the bright sunshine, looking with wide eyes at the colorful sights of the beautiful Italian city which was like a fairy-tale adventure to her, the girl returned to the hotel. Mrs. Gilbert, seeing her without the boy, asked quickly, "Where is Bab?"

"Is—isn't—why, he's with you, isn't he?" faltered the maid.

Mr. Gilbert came up. "What's the trouble? Where's William?" he asked the two pale women.

The maid burst into tears. "I don't know. You see—" And she told the story of the charming Italians.

"We don't know any such men," Mr. Gilbert informed her.

Mrs. Gilbert, realizing that nothing more or less than a kidnapping had taken place, buried her face in her hands and sobbed.

Meanwhile, the boy William was being taken horseback along a picturesque road to the hills. The two pleasant Italian gentlemen rode furiously until they came to a cluster of poor little huts. This was the headquarters of a group of brigands, who, in the best romantic-novel style, waylaid unwary travelers, taking their purses and jewelry. They varied the program occasionally by holding for ransom a foreign child like William.

The police of Naples shrugged their shoulders when they were urged to do something about the kidnapping, and said, "Don't worry. It will probably turn out all right."

In due course a note reached the distracted parents in Naples. They might buy back their son, it read, for the sum of twenty-five pounds (about $125.00). The money was promptly given into the hands of the mysterious messenger, and William, who had received good care and who had, on the whole, enjoyed his excursion into the hills, was returned to his family as casually as he had been abducted.

When it was all over, the adventure seemed less serious than fantastic and humorous. The ease with which two charming strangers had deceived the simple nursemaid, the calm indifference of the Italian authorities, and the easy confidence of the brigands in collecting the ransom and returning the child made a good story to tell friends in England. Everyone had to laugh at the small ransom figure, and Bab was chaffed for having been valued so cheaply.

William and his three sisters heard the story many times. It lost nothing in the telling, for Mr. Gilbert, who was a man with a rather bizarre imagination, did a little weaving and embroidering of his own to add color to the simple story. "All in all," he would declare with a twinkle in his eye, and an affectionate glance at his son, "the twenty-five pounds we paid to get him back was a good investment."

Just how good an investment young William was, his father had no way of foreseeing. If the boy had not been returned by the brigands, England would have lost a future humorist and playwright of great significance. This young William called *Bab* was to be the author of the most popular nonsense verse in the English language, the *Bab Ballads*. More important still, he was to be associated with the English composer Arthur Seymour Sullivan in a collaboration which produced the wittiest and gayest comic operas ever written—the Savoy operas as they were called, after the famous theater where most of them were produced.

Gilbert and Sullivan. They were a team, and what a team! Gilbert wrote the words. Sullivan set them to music. Working like one man, and that man a genius, they created the fourteen famous comic operas or operettas which have been called the "golden fourteen." *The Pirates of Penzance. H.M.S. Pinafore. The Mikado. The Yeomen of the Guard. The Gondoliers.* Wherever English is spoken, the music of these operas is sung and their verses are quoted. English to the core, Gilbert's humor and wit make the songs and dialogue of the librettos as untranslatable into any other language as Lewis Carroll's *Song of the Jabberwocky.* And Sullivan's settings seem to spring like the daisies beloved of Chaucer and the cowslips of Shakespeare from the English soil itself.

A man with a comic-opera abduction to start him off in life could hardly have been expected to be as other men—and Gilbert wasn't. All his life he was a "character," as unpredictable and wayward as the plots of his amusing and topsy-turvy stories. He had a temper. He had a sharp tongue. He was funny, but he often lacked a sense of humor. And he was sentimental.

He lived in Victorian England, where the theater was considered not quite respectable; yet he made his living by writing for the stage and was ultimately knighted for his work as a playwright. His serious plays were so bathetic and sentimental that today they seem absurd, but Gilbert never saw their absurdity and was always apologetic for the fact that his humor rather than his gravity made him rich. He bought an expensive Tudor house and a hundred twenty-five acres with the royalties from his comedies and operettas; yet he spoke of his estate cynically as "a monument to English folly."

He liked pretty ladies and children and animals, and for them he had only sweet temper and kindness; but he could be unspeakably rude to elderly women, and with most of his men contemporaries he was not on speaking terms. He could write a comic-opera libretto making fun of the whole idea of breach-of-promise suits, and then busy himself whole-heartedly with helping an actress friend win such a case in real life.

He criticized actors, managers, critics—everyone; but the mildest criticism of his own work or conduct threw him into a passion. He once went to actor Beerbohm-Tree's dressing room after a performance of *Hamlet*.

"How did you like it?" the actor asked.

"Never saw anything so funny in my life, and yet it was not in the least vulgar," said Gilbert promptly.

For an actor who had tried his best to interpret a serious rôle with high art, this was the sort of sneering criticism not likely to cement friendship.

Gilbert never ceased to wonder at the number of enemies such remarks created. However, when an old friend, Clement Scott, repeated a mild joke of F. Burnand's in which Gilbert's play *Broken Hearts* was referred to as *Broken Parts*, Gilbert never spoke to Scott again.

He could be delightfully whimsical, as in his invitation to a grown-up young lady to go sailing on his yacht, the *Pleione*. With mock-seriousness, he wrote:

"You will so order yourself in all things as to tend most effectually to my bodily and mental comfort.

"You will wear your best hat.

"You will do your hair high on your head like a coco-nut—but not too high. . . .

"You will be careful to have *clean nails and knuckles,* and that no tapes are dragging below your dress. Also to wear neat boots and gloves. And in these matters, fail not your friend,

W. S. Gilbert"

At dinner the same day he was quite capable of saying maliciously to an elderly lady pretending to be too young to remember the Crimean War, "I'm sure you could if you tried!"

Then, just as his associates in the theater had made up their minds that the crusty, high-tempered, high-handed playwright was an insufferable egoist, he would make fun of himself. In his seventieth year, Gilbert made a speech at a banquet in his honor. Quoting from one of his own works, he remarked dryly, "Everybody says I'm such a disagreeable man, and I can't think why!" The banqueters burst into roars of appreciative laughter. If Gilbert, because of his sarcasms and bossiness, was the most disliked man in London, at least he was also its most beloved dramatist and librettist. Of *that* there was

". . . no manner of doubt—
No probable, possible shadow of doubt—
No possible doubt whatever."

Gilbert was born in London, at No. 17 Southampton Street, Strand, on November 18th, 1836. That was just a year before Victoria ascended the throne of England, to begin her long reign of sixty-four years. Victoria proved herself to be a "right-down regular Royal Queen," whose strong personality, firm religious faith, and stuffy, conservative ideas of art and conduct so influenced her subjects that the last six decades of the nineteenth century have been labeled the Victorian period. In an insular English world of heavy, hideous house furnishings, drab, uninteresting dress, and dull church sermons, Gilbert was to develop into a naughty, rebellious Victorian *enfant terrible,* a thorn in the royal side. Everyone in Victorian England that *was* someone was a little ashamed of him, but they laughed just the same.

He was named William for his father, and Schwenck after his godmother. It was characteristic of Gilbert that though he thoroughly disliked his middle name, he disliked even more the careless persons who left out either of the two c's or otherwise tampered with the curious spelling of it.

One thing is sure. Gilbert came by his crotchety disposition naturally. His father was a droll, eccentric person, and his mother, of whom little is known, was at least able to put up with her husband's oddities, and so may be assumed to have been somewhat out of the ordinary herself.

William Gilbert, Sr., at fourteen became a midshipman in the service of the East India Company. That was in 1818. After a difference of opinion with his employers over the question of human rights, concerning which this particular William held some very strong ideas, he gave up his job and went wandering about Europe. He came home in 1825 and matriculated as a student in Guy's Hospital, becoming at length a naval surgeon. He was still in his twenties when an inheritance from his father allowed him to retire.

With his wife, three daughters, and young son well provided for, he varied a program of idleness and travel with writing. As he grew older, he made writing his chief hobby. No subject was sacred. He attacked everything from the Catholic Church to the fashionable ladies' doctor "who never cures." He wrote romantic novels, children's stories, biographies, plays, political satires, and fairy tales—most of them so dull that it is hard to understand where the publishers were found who issued the books. Eventually the senior Gilbert's works became so numerous that their titles alone fill almost two columns of the British Museum index.

It is a curious fact that although he did much writing in his twenties and thirties, most of his books were written and published after he was forty. This was after his son was a well-known writer, too. The younger Gilbert once remarked, "You see, my father never had an exaggerated idea of my abilities; he thought if I could write, anybody could, and forthwith began to do so." Even though he made light of his parent's efforts, Gilbert, a self-taught sketch artist, illustrated two of his own books. These were the children's stories, *The Magic Mirror* and *King George's Middy.*

In the Gilbert home there was always a number of artists, authors, and musicians being entertained. The dinner hour never lacked for fantastic and romantic story and anecdote, with the elder Gilbert making the most of his relationship to the Elizabethan navigator Sir Humphrey Gilbert, and holding forth at length on his favorite subjects of insanity and murder. During the day, however, there was no time for nonsense or romance. The father's work hours at his writing desk were respected almost religiously by both family and guests. It was a strange home atmosphere, where fantasy rubbed shoulders with a pompous, almost unimaginative, and certainly humorless daily round of tasks.

When he was seven years old, William was sent to school at Boulogne, France. Why his parents chose a French school remains a mystery. At any rate, it is obvious that the six years he spent there were part and parcel of his topsy-turvy boyhood, and bore fruit later in the topsy-turvy operas.

One important bit of knowledge came to young Gilbert out of the French experience: An understanding of French poetry and French verse forms, especially the double rhyme with the last syllable unaccented, known as "feminine rhyme." The amusing rhyme pattern of such a song as Katisha's and Ko-Ko's in *The Mikado* gives a gay musical swing to the words:

> "If that is so,
>   Sing derry down derry!
>   It's evident very,
>   Our tastes are one.
>   Away we'll go,
>   And merrily marry,
>   Nor tardily tarry
>   Till day is done!"

When he was thirteen, young William was brought back to England to attend the Great Ealing School, where such famous men as William Makepeace Thackeray, John Henry Newman, and Thomas Huxley had learned their history and grammar. Very little is recorded of the days at Great Ealing. William ran away once and tried to go on the stage, but was promptly sent back to his desk by actor Charles Kean, who turned out to be a friend of William's father. After that, he settled down to serious study and writing an occasional play for his schoolfellows. Gilbert's only comment in after years was, "I was not a popular boy, I believe."

From Great Ealing he went to King's College, Cambridge, intending to finish his studies at Oxford. But the year was 1855, and the Crimean War had begun. Gilbert decided to take the examinations for an officer's commission. He entered the University of London to get his B.A. degree, and began to cram for the army tests.

Before the examinations were held, however, the war came to an end; so instead of adding himself, perhaps, to the English cemetery at Balaklava, he added himself to the clerical staff of the Education Department of the English Privy Council Office. He hated his clerk's job fiercely for four long years. When he inherited three hundred pounds from an aunt, he lost no time in leaving the Education Department and taking up law. ". . . on the happiest day of my life I sent in my resignation," he wrote in later years.

Meanwhile, he satisfied his thwarted military ambitions by joining the 5th West Yorks Militia. A few years later, he was transferred to the Royal Aberdeenshire Militia. In 1875, this regiment won the privilege of wearing the kilt, with the Gordon tartan, and were known as the Gordon Highlanders. Gilbert, who became a captain and remained with his plaid-clad Highlanders for nearly fourteen years, always made a handsome figure in his picturesque Scottish uniform, though story has it that he took the discipline rather lightly.

Once when he took his men on maneuvers in Scotland, the day was damp in the extreme, raw and cold. Gilbert disliked the idea of tramping all day in a downpour. It had been decided to have part of the regiment hide out in the wet heather-covered hills while the other half tried to track them down. Gilbert was in charge of the hunted party. When they were out of sight and sound of the "hunters," he brought his men back to the warm inn fires. The hunting party tramped all day in a fruitless search for Gilbert's very comfortable soldiers. What his colonel, in charge of the hunting group, said to Gilbert on discovering the trick has never been recorded.

There followed the youthful Bohemian period of studying law in the Temple, sharing his living quarters with another young barrister, and practicing law for four years with an average of five clients per year. When Gilbert wrote his song about a "briefless barrister" in his *Trial by Jury,* he was writing about something he knew very well. There were one or two amusing and several painful appearances in court, and Gilbert bowed out of the legal profession.

The story is told of his inviting some friends to witness one of his cases, the defence of an Irish woman on trial for being drunk and disorderly. The young barrister rose to present his client's case, but he had not had time to utter two words when the woman decided that he was not the lawyer for her.

"Don't believe a word he says, yer Honor," she shrieked. "He's drunk! Sit down, ye spalpeen!"

Red of face, poor Gilbert sat down amid the roars of laughter.

The truth of the matter is, Gilbert was paying very little attention to his briefs. He was already on the road to a new and more exciting profession, that of writing. His first "published" work appeared on the program of a concert in which a singer he had known for many years, Mademoiselle Parepa, was to appear. She wanted to sing the laughing song from *Manon Lescaut* in English, and asked Gilbert to make a translation for her from the French. He produced some excellent lines:

> "An entertaining story,
> A fiction amatory,
> About a legal star,
> Ha! ha! ha! ha! ha! ha!
> A legal dignitary
> Particularly wary,
> A member of the bar,
> Ha! ha! ha! ha! ha! ha!"

Gilbert later told the story of how he went night after night to hear his translation sung. He would watch the faces of those reading the printed words in their programs, and think to himself, "How amazed and delighted they would be if they were aware that the gifted creature who made the translation is standing so near them!"

The translation was given to the world in 1857. In 1861, when a magazine called *Fun* was launched, he sent some verses and pen drawings to the editor, H. J. Byron, who immediately asked for regular contributions. To this magazine went the unique series of comic ballads illustrated with grotesque wood cuts signed "Bab" which today are known as the *Bab Ballads*. Ingenious, funny, clever in rhyme and thought, the series began with the familiar *The Yarn of the Nancy Bell,* which was turned down by the editor of *Punch* because it was "too cannibalistic" for his readers' tastes. Victorian England of the 1860's was not ready for a cheerful sailor who confessed to having eaten his fellow mariners, thereby becoming the mate and the captain bold and the stout crew, too, of the good ship *Nancy Bell.*

The *Bab Ballads* have some amazing comments on nearly every subject under the sun. Their author wrote about the sea; about curates and bishops; about military men; about courts of law; about Scotsmen; about fairies; about babies changed in their cradles, kidnapped, or put out to nurse; about actors; about any and everything and nothing, too, as he sat in his law office and waited for the briefs to come "trooping gaily."

He composed a verse or two about a certain Martin Tupper, who had written a book of incredibly dull rhymed proverbs of which Queen Victoria was fond. In answer to a query put to this illustrious Tupper, according to the ballad:

"Mr. Tupper sent the following reply to me:—
'A fool is bent upon the twig, but wise men dread a bandit.'
Which I think must have been clever, for I didn't understand it."

Young Gilbert was on the way to becoming the royal thorn.

One of the legal ballads has never ceased to please those whose opinion of attorneys is not high:

"Whene'er he heard a tale of woe
From client A or client B,
His grief would overcome him so,
He'd scarce have strength to take his fee."

Gilbert always maintained that he had no ear for music. He declared that he knew two tunes. One was *God Save the King,* and the other wasn't. The *Bab Ballads* argue against him. They are extremely musical, showing the author's sensitivity to the sound of words and his perfect sense of rhythm. *Prince Agib* has some musical foolery in delightfully musical form:

"They played him a sonata—let me see!
'*Medulla oblongata*'—key of G.
Then they began to sing
That extremely lovely thing,
'*Scherzando! ma non troppo. ppp.*'"

During these ballad days, Gilbert moved to chambers in Gray's
Inn, where the group of journalists, dramatists, and critics that
clustered around Byron and *Fun* began to visit him. Gilbert suggested that they form a club, with annual dues of two guineas, he
himself to be exempted on the understanding that he should
furnish a steak pie, a joint of cold beef, a Stilton cheese, whisky
and soda and ale every Saturday night for the rest of his life.
Gilbert had to buy popularity, it seems.

The club was called "The Serious Family." It included H. J.
Byron, Tom Hood, who succeeded him as editor of *Fun,* the critic
Clement Scott, Artemus Ward, the humorist, and Tom Robert-
son, the playwright.

Gilbert struck up an intimate friendship with Tom Robertson,
who was beginning to show London how a play should be produced. Robertson, the author of *Caste* and a number of other
"realistic" dramas, was the first stage director in England to dress
his interior sets to look like real rooms. Tables, chairs, windows,
lights, cups and saucers—everything as in a real home—were an
innovation in his day. Gilbert watched his friend at work, and
learned his methods. When he became his own director, Gilbert
admitted that he owed much to Robertson.

It was Robertson, in fact, who encouraged Gilbert to write for
the stage and even arranged for his first effort to be produced.
This was a burlesque of a French work. It was called *Dulcamara;*

or, The Little Duck and the Great Quack, and was written to
order as a Christmas piece for St. James's Theatre, in 1866.

By the time this first play of his was produced Gilbert was sure
enough of his earning power to propose marriage to a girl he had
known for three years. On August 6th, 1867, he was married to
Miss Lucy Turner, the daughter of an officer in the Indian service. The Bohemian days of Gray's Inn came to an end. Gilbert
and his wife went to live in a villa in Kensington.

The theater managers watched the success of *Dulcamara,* and,
unlike the briefs which had not come his way, the commissions
to write comic take-offs and lampoons of serious plays and operas
came in regularly. Gilbert learned his trade well in the years
when he was writing burlesques for manager John Hollingshead,
of the Gaiety Theatre, and tame little skits with innocent puns for
the Thomas German Reeds.

Only Victorian England could have produced an institution
like the German Reeds and their Gallery of Illustration. They
came into being because of the popular prejudice against the
theater, in which comedy had degenerated from the high stand-
ards of an earlier day. Comedy in the sixties meant risqué French
farce, or burlesques which were either poor translations of Offenbach's operas or hodge-podges of broadly comic verse set to exist-
ing folk tunes. The comedian with a big, false nose, the chambermaid with absurdly short skirt, the songs with atrocious puns and
vulgar double meanings—these made up the fare of the music
halls. The Victorians were right to reject it, but they made the
mistake of condemning the popular theater on moral rather than
on aesthetic grounds. Instead of demanding better fare, they
chose to go on a hunger strike.

Gilbert wrote a sarcastic article protesting all this. In *Actors,*

Authors, and Audiences he lashed out at managers, low comedians, temperamental actresses, and singing comediennes alike. An author is on trial for having written a stupid play. His defence is that his play was not so stupid before the manager and actors began to change it. He cross-examines those who butchered his lines, beginning with the manager, who says:

"I did not read your play before accepting it, because I do not profess to be a judge of a play in manuscript . . . I have no special training for the position of manager. I am not aware that any special training is requisite."

The leading lady declares, "I have never been hissed in my life. The parts I have played have frequently been hissed. No one has ever hissed *me.*"

The low comedian tells the author, "I did my best with the part. I bought a remarkably clever mechanical wig."

The singing chambermaid explains, "The part I played was that of a simple-minded young governess in a country rectory, who is secretly in love with the Home Secretary. I did not see why such a character should not sing and dance in the intervals between her pathetic scenes. I do not consider 'Father's pants will soon fit brother' an inappropriate song for such a character."

This was brutally frank, not far from a true picture of the senseless, tasteless amusement tolerated by an England which seemed to have forgotten the heritage of Shakespeare, Congreve, Goldsmith, and Sheridan. The German Reeds set themselves the task of correcting this absurd situation. They understood their contemporaries. They knew that there was a large number of respectable people who longed to go to a theater. The Victorians wanted to laugh and enjoy light music, but they believed—or at least they were afraid that their friends and neighbors believed—

that to attend a theater was a sin. The German Reeds were sure that such people would coöperate in a little hypocritical cover-up. The Victorians understood nothing so well as the art of deceiving their consciences.

Why not open a theater and call it something else? reasoned the Reeds. In St. Martin's Hall, their company of two opened with "Miss P. Horton's Illustrative Gatherings." Their skits, readings, and songs could have been presented at any young ladies' boarding school, but they had humor and charm, too, in addition to their high moral tone. Victorian London, hungry for a little fun, came in such numbers to the hall that the German Reeds had to move to larger quarters. They opened, not a theater, but a Gallery of Illustration in Regent Street. More artists were added to their company of two, until they had a regular light-opera troupe. The "wicked" orchestra was omitted, however. A piano and churchly harmonium provided the accompaniment for the singers, a bit of sly deception practiced on a church-going audience used to organs and choirs.

Fred Clay, a genial composer of songs and comic operas, wrote the music for one of the best skits which Gilbert prepared for the unique establishment of the German Reeds. Clay's talent was of the ready, occasional sort. Today he is remembered for his *I'll sing thee songs of Araby* from his cantata *Lalla Rookh*. He was just the composer for the Gallery of Illustration, and did a good job of setting Gilbert's *Ages Ago*. The skit proved so popular that Clay proudly invited his composer friend Arthur Seymour Sullivan to come round to Regent Street to see it. Sullivan did, and Clay introduced him to Gilbert. This was in 1869.

Clay's introduction of Sullivan to Gilbert seemed of little or no significance at the time. An already famous composer and a

successful playwright met, exchanged a few pleasant words, and
went their ways. But several producers remembered seeing the
two together. It was John Hollingshead of the Gaiety Theatre who
did something about it. He brought Gilbert and Sullivan together
as librettist and composer for a comic opera called *Thespis; or,
The Gods Grown Old.*

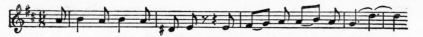

And to your hu-mours chang-ing I tune my sup-ple song!

2

ULLIVAN was six years Gilbert's junior; yet when they met in 1869 he was already the more famous of the two. A brilliant student career was behind him. He was a popular writer of songs. He had composed considerable serious music, notably the incidental music for Shakespeare's *The Tempest,* and a symphony *(The Irish)* which had won him the acclaim of the most celebrated men of music of his day. Unlike Gilbert, however, he did not come from a home where inheritances provided ease and comfort and expensive schooling. He had only his genius and a capacity for hard work for "capital." Making the most of both, he had lifted himself by the bootstraps out of pinching poverty.

His father, Thomas Sullivan, was the son of an Irish soldier who had been one of the guards at St. Helena during Napoleon Bonaparte's exile. Thomas was born on St. Helena, and as a little boy accompanied the former emperor on his walks about the island prison.

Sullivan's mother, Maria Clementina Coghlan, was of Irish and Italian ancestry. Her mother's family were the artistic Righis, one of whom was Michelangelo's principal assistant.

Thomas and Maria Clementina were both working in London when they met. They were engaged to be married many years before there was money enough to establish a home. Thomas worked as a clarinet player in the Surrey Theatre, where grand opera was performed. He earned the munificent sum of a guinea a week (about $5.11). He increased his small income by doing music copying on the side. Maria helped her father and mother in a small private school which they managed.

Early in the year 1839, the two poor young people were married, and established their modest home at No. 8, Bolwell Terrace. Their first son, Fred, was born on Christmas Day, and though his coming brought joy to the young parents, it brought also a serious problem. The small income of Thomas Sullivan could not be stretched to care for three persons. It is a sad comment on the starvation wages of the day that the young mother had to take a position as governess in a wealthy household and give her own baby into the care of a cheap nursery. It took the Sullivans four years to increase their income sufficiently for the family to be reunited.

Another son was born to them in 1842, on May 13th. They named him Arthur Seymour. Though they were now four, and the pinch of poverty was great, Thomas Sullivan somehow managed to keep his family together under one roof. His wage at the Surrey remained as meager as ever, but by working long hours at music copying, the necessary food and clothing, rent and fuel were provided. The great love of the parents for each other, and the affection between children and parents, made the poor house a rich home.

When Arthur was three years old and Fred seven, their father was appointed bandmaster at the Royal Military College at Sandhurst. Writing of this new position and its larger salary, Thomas Sullivan said: "The change drew me out of the awful life of sameness. It was like the coming of a new day."

Thomas Sullivan was an excellent musician, with a thorough understanding of band instruments and military music. His youth had not been spent with the old soldier of St. Helena for nothing. His colonel at Sandhurst said of him, "Sullivan is one of the most remarkable people we have ever had here. He is what we have lacked—a real musician."

It is not strange that Thomas' two sons should be influenced by their father's work. Fred became a violoncellist of considerable skill, and a singer with a talent for comedy. Though he at first took up architecture to make his living, Fred eventually abandoned this vocation for the stage. He sang in his brother's first two comic operas. As he said wittily, he still drew big houses.

Arthur, for his part, attended every rehearsal at Sandhurst, and learned to play every instrument in the band. With equal ease, he played the flute, clarinet, alt-horn, French horn, cornet, trombone, and euphonium. As for his voice, he had a sweet, true soprano, capable of reaching high A with ease.

When Arthur was old enough to go to school, he was enrolled at the private academy of William Gordon Plees, in Bishop's Road, Bayswater, where he stayed from his eighth until his twelfth year. Even in those early years he had that uncanny genius for making friends which distinguished him as a youth and man. Everyone at Mr. Plees' school liked the short, stocky, dark-haired boy with the smiling eyes and sober mouth.

Perhaps it was his instinct for doing the kindly, considerate thing which won friendship. A letter written to his mother when

he was ten years old shows him to have been a child with more
than ordinary dignity and responsibility:

"I say," he began it. "I want to speak to you. One of our boys,
Higham, has taken a great fancy to my knife. He has a little
gold pencil-case which I have taken a great fancy to. He asked
me whether, if he gives me the pencil-case and a two-bladed knife,
will I give him mine. I have submitted this to your discre-
tion."

Young Arthur's interest in singing led him to read the lives of
famous musicians. A number of England's greatest had received
their training in the Chapel Royal. It was not long before the
boy's letters home included earnest entreaties to be allowed to
become a chorister.

Arthur's parents were at first firm in their refusal, since they
believed that the musical demands of the Chapel Royal would
interfere with the boy's general education. Arthur's pleading became more and more insistent. "It means everything to me!" he
wrote, and they gave in.

In 1854, kindly Mr. Plees and his twelve-year-old pupil went to
see Sir George Smart, composer and organist for the Chapel
Royal. Sir George heard the boy sing and knew at once that a
great talent was knocking at the door of the Chapel. He sent
Arthur and his teacher to see the Reverend Thomas Helmore, who
was in charge of the choristers.

Thomas Helmore, conscientious teacher of boys, whose heart
was as warm as his manner was dour, liked both Arthur and his
voice. He was astonished at the boy's knowledge of music and
musical instruments. There was but one difficulty. New boys had
to be under nine years. Arthur was twelve. Thomas Helmore,
who was not the man to go about breaking rules, actually re-

quested the sub-Dean to break that one. Arthur received his coveted appointment to the Chapel Royal.

He stayed with the other choristers at Mr. Helmore's house, where he was taught grammar as well as music. He sang in the choir twice on Sundays and Saints' Days at St. James's Palace. With the others he was sent to sing at royal christenings, weddings, and memorial services. When the first Handel Festival was held at Crystal Palace, Arthur and his companions in the Chapel sang in the huge choir.

Thomas Helmore was a strict teacher of the old-time school. He pounded Latin and music alike into his young pupils with a liberal use of the rod, but he knew talent when he saw it, and he knew how to encourage it, too. He was quick to perceive Arthur's special gift, and wrote to his pupil's mother:

"He should do every week about twelve exercises and compose a little something. . . ."

The teacher's confidence was not misplaced. Arthur's first ambitious composition was written and sung in 1855, during his choristership. This was the anthem *Sing Unto the Lord and Praise His Name*. Sullivan often said in later years that Helmore was the greatest teacher of his youth.

There was plenty of work for the boys at the Chapel Royal, but there was fun, too. Arthur wrote home about a band which they had organized. They played on combs and other absurd make-believe instruments. Arthur took his place by common consent as leader of this band and composer for it. His first songs were written in these early years when he conducted the comb band. A letter to his mother indicates that he actually sold some of them, to admiring princes and others who heard him sing his own sacred compositions in the Chapel.

His letters home contained references to a varied program of amusement—fireworks, a concert of Anton Rubinstein's, a holiday outing in Devonshire, a concert of Jenny Lind's, a chemical set. With all his talent, it was obvious that he had the knack of remaining unspoiled and normal.

With Queen Victoria as usual setting the fashion, London of this day knew but two composers—Handel for church, Mendelssohn for drawing room. Felix Mendelssohn had been Victoria's music teacher. On Sunday evenings at Windsor, the Queen played her beloved master's music and little else. In his honor, a scholarship had been established to aid young musicians.

In 1856, a momentous announcement was made by the committee for the Mendelssohn Scholarship. For the first time, it was to be awarded on the basis of a competitive examination.

Arthur was in fever to enter the lists. He was the youngest of seventeen contestants who reached the "finals." Hardly daring to hope that he might win, he determined nevertheless "to make a fight for it."

At the competition in London, he tied with seventeen-year-old Joseph Barnby, who in later years became one of his best friends. A second and more exacting contest was arranged to decide between the two. Sullivan won. The letter which told him of his good fortune was immediately framed and remained one of his prized possessions all his life.

His good father received the news at Kneller Hall, the training school for military bands where he had taught clarinet since his promotion from Sandhurst in 1857. Thomas Sullivan loved music, too, even though for him it had been a hard and often cruel taskmistress. This honor for one of his beloved sons was to this unselfish man ample reward for his own hard work and his devotion to his art. Writing to his wife, he begged: "Bring the darling little fellow down with you if you can for a day or two. I long to embrace him. Kiss him a thousand times for me."

The Mendelssohn award enabled Arthur to attend the Royal Academy of Music, with all expenses paid for one year. He had lessons on the piano from William Sterndale Bennett and Arthur O'Leary, and lessons in harmony from John Goss. Since he did not play any orchestral instrument, he began to study violin. He wrote his parents, "I am also going to try to learn Italian." For a poor boy, this scholarship opened the portals of music. No wonder both his parents wept for joy when their son achieved what had seemed impossible.

During the year 1856–57, when he was attending the Academy, Arthur kept up his duties in the Chapel Royal. Between the two, he had little time for anything but music. Gradually mention of the fireworks and chemical sets disappeared from his letters. When in 1857 the scholarship was unexpectedly renewed, Arthur was a serious student with one goal before him—to perfect himself in his art. The piano was his chosen instrument.

Both Arthur and Fred, who at this time was finishing his studies in architecture, were as poor as church mice. There is a pathetic letter written by Arthur for the two of them to their mother on her birthday, which, because Maria Clementina was the mother she was, must have been more valuable to her than the most expensive gift:

"Fred and I have been ruminating for the last half-hour what to say to you on this happy occasion. May God bless you and keep you to see many more brighter and happier years than this has been. We have no presents to offer you, but as a small token of affection, if you like to keep that 30s. you owe us for singing money you are quite at liberty to lay it out in whatever way you like."

The scholarship committee had something up their sleeves. They did not tell young Sullivan what it was, but gave him a hint when they suggested that it would be a good idea to study German. The wife of the Honorary Secretary of the Mendelssohn Committee, Mrs. Klingmann, offered to tutor him free of charge. The young student applied himself dutifully to his German verbs, and before his second year at the Academy was over, he was informed that the scholarship had been renewed for another year—a year to be spent in study at the famous Conservatory of Music at Leipzig, Germany, a school founded by Mendelssohn himself.

It seemed like a dream, a dream too good to be true, but it was true. Young Sullivan packed his best clothes, said goodbye to his family and the friends at the Academy and Royal Chapel, and boarded a Channel boat for the exciting trip to the Continent. He reached Leipzig in September, 1858. That was the same fall that Edvard Grieg, who became Norway's greatest composer, set out from Bergen to study at the Conservatory at Leipzig.

Sullivan, like Grieg, whom he came to know and like, found the German city of Leipzig strange and a little frightening. Homesick for the family in England, understanding and speaking the German language imperfectly, he was lonesome at first. But work and music soon made him forget his personal problems; letters from home eased his loneliness, and his own sunny, humorous nature won him friends in plenty in the foreign city.

Very soon he was quite at home in the narrow, winding streets of old Leipzig. He lost no time in visiting all the spots sacred to music—Thomaskirche, where Johann Sebastian Bach had been organist; Auerbach Hof of Goethe's *Faust* fame, and the Gewand. haus. Mendelssohn in the years 1835 to 1843 had made the concerts in the Gewandhaus famous throughout the world. In doing so, he had given new life to an institution which was the oldest of its kind. The Gewandhaus concerts dated from the time that Bach was Cantor of Thomasschule.

In establishing the Conservatory of Leipzig, Mendelssohn had set a pattern of excellence and brilliance. In his day the best teachers and musicians were persuaded to join the faculty. Many of them, ten years after the founder's death, remained to teach boys like Arthur from England and Edvard from Norway. Newcomers to the faculty had to measure up to the early standard of Mendelssohn.

In the year that Grieg and Sullivan came to Leipzig, Herr Conrad Schleinitz was the Director of the Conservatory. Ignaz Moscheles, Mendelssohn's old teacher and a friend of Beethoven, was still there, and Moritz Hauptmann, the grand old man of music, was still tutoring a few advanced students in his rooms in Bach's old residence. Richter, David, Rietz, Plaidy, Wenzel— these were among the famous teachers for the talented youngsters at Leipzig.

Ernst Wenzel spoke English; consequently, most of the English-speaking students were in his class. In Sullivan's day these included five who were to become distinguished musicians: John Franklin Taylor and Walter Bacher, pianists; Edward Dannreuther, pianist and champion of Wagner in England; John Francis Barnett, famous teacher. Carl Rosa and Fred Clay, both destined to be associated with England's comic opera, were also fellow students of Sullivan's.

Wenzel was an inspired teacher. Grieg said of him, "Above all, there was music behind his words." He had been a fellow-student and friend of Robert Schumann's at the old Leipzig University. In Sullivan's student days, the music of both Schumann and Schubert was ignored by the musicians of the "classic" school of thought. There was hardly a musician in England who had any use for either. From teachers like Wenzel, Sullivan learned about these composers of the new "Romantic" school. Later he made it his mission to introduce them to an English public whose musical taste had congealed with Mendelssohn.

Sullivan, who knew how to appreciate art wherever he found it, worshipped at a number of shrines: Mozart, Beethoven, Weber, Mendelssohn, Schubert, Schumann. From the works of these composers he learned how music is put together. Of them all, the balance and symmetry of the genius of Mozart were most nearly akin to his own talents.

He never learned to like Richard Wagner's operas, however. With the exception of *Die Meistersinger,* which he once spoke of as the greatest comic opera ever written, he found Wagner's works dull and coarse. He stoutly maintained that the characters of *Das Rheingold* were nothing but "liars, thieves, and black-guards." He described *Siegfried* as "puerile drivel," and dismissed *Die Götterdämmerung* as "dull and dreary."

Sullivan entered the Conservatory with but one ambition, to become the best concert pianist of his day. As soon as he studied with Ferdinand David, he changed his plan in favor of becoming a conductor. He wrote of this new scheme to his old friend of the Chapel Royal, Sir George Smart, and received an amusing but somewhat damping reply:

"As to your becoming a conductor, that office is not so lucrative in this country as it was in former years, for there are so many conductors that some of them are non-conductors."

Making every penny go as far as possible, Sullivan shared rooms with John Franklin Taylor, denied himself fuel for his fire until the cold of the northern German city made his fingers too numb to work, and economized on meals. His many friendships were both a help and an embarrassment. He referred half-humorously in one of his letters home to the fact that invitations to dinner saved him money. At Christmas time, however, the necessity to remember his friends with gifts taxed his poor purse to the limit.

Another letter is both amusing and pathetic. It shows Sullivan to have been an unusual youngster, in that he could continue his social life despite lack of good clothes. Many boys would have drawn into their shells.

"Ask Father if I ought to have a new coat," he wrote Fred. ". . . having worn this one a whole year, almost every day, the nap has all worn off, and if I want to go for a walk with the Moscheles or Davids I am obliged to put on my dress-suit, which of course, besides wearing out, looks so absurd in the afternoon."

At the end of his first year, the reports of Sullivan's professors at Leipzig were so favorable that the Committee in England renewed his scholarship for another year. To show his gratitude, the boy composed an anthem *We Have Heard With Our Ears* and dedicated it to the head of the Committee, Sir George Smart, his stanchest friend. This was the year 1860, and Sullivan had already given up the idea of being a conductor in favor of becoming a composer. Encouragement in this choice was given him by his beloved teacher Julius Rietz. When Rietz left to take up a post in Dresden that year, Sullivan wrote to his parents, "Poor

Rietz, I'm sorry he's gone . . . he was a splendid master and very kind to me."

Sullivan was composing incessantly, though much of what he accomplished was practice work. In June, one of his compositions, *Overture to T. Moore's Poem "The Feast of Roses"* was publicly performed at a Conservatory Prüfung, with the boy proudly conducting his own work.

In August of that year, a spectacular storm struck Leipzig. Sullivan described it vividly in a letter:

". . . the air became hot and oppressive. . . . Then came the long distant moans of the wind, a few thick large raindrops, and finally the whole storm broke out with wild fury, such as the oldest inhabitant declared never to have seen the like of. . . . Chimney pots were falling, tiles rolling down, windows smashing. Women and children screaming. Horses taking fright and running away. In fact, everybody imagining that the Last Day had come . . ."

There is no doubt that the impression made by this real storm influenced the music of his incidental score for Shakespeare's *The Tempest,* which he began to compose soon afterward.

Mendelssohn had composed incidental music for Shakespeare's *Midsummer Night's Dream* when he was seventeen. Sullivan at eighteen chose to try his hand at a similar task. It is not surprising that the music for *The Tempest* shows throughout the influence of Mendelssohn's style. With his enthusiastic championship of Schubert and Schumann, he might have been expected to mirror one of them in his first serious work, but, whether consciously or unconsciously, he chose instead to turn to the founder of the Conservatory for his model. It was a courtly tribute, a graceful paying of a debt.

At the end of that summer of 1860, the second year of his

scholarship at Leipzig was up. Sullivan prepared to pack his bags, rather sadly, for all the teachers told him that he would profit much by staying until Easter of the following year. Arthur had mentioned the fact in a letter home, but had hastened to add that he knew how impossible it would be to arrange for the extra study.

Thomas Sullivan was not one to do things by halves. He was earning a little extra money by teaching four night classes a week. He managed to scrape together enough money to keep Arthur in school for the extra months. Surprised at this turn of fortune, and humbly grateful to the parents who were making the sacrifice for him, Arthur wrote with tears in his eyes:

". . . I will try to make the end of your days happy and comfortable." He never forgot that promise, and was thankful that his music allowed him to keep it.

The Director of the Conservatory also made a generous gesture by exempting Arthur from fees for the rest of his stay. His spirits buoyed up by all this good luck and friendship, the young composer began to score his music for *The Tempest*. The April of 1861, just before he started home for good, his composition was performed at Leipzig. It was a huge success, and Sullivan was called forward three times by the enthusiastic audience. That was his goodbye to the student days. With the manuscript in his bag and the music in his brain representing his total assets, he set out to conquer London.

First of all, of course, he visited his parents and Fred. Then he made a "sentimental journey" through his old haunts, the Chapel Royal and the Royal Academy of Music. Cipriani Potter was head of the Academy at the time. For this "dear old man, with beetling eyebrows and high stuck-up collars," good music had stopped with Beethoven. Young Sullivan's ardent praise of Schumann resulted only in heated arguments until one day Sullivan said to the old fellow, "Have you ever heard any of this music you condemn?"

Potter admitted that he had not. Sullivan produced some of Schumann's symphonies arranged for four hands. The result of their playing these together was that Potter became the chief advocate of Schumann in England.

About this time Sullivan met George Grove, Secretary of the Crystal Palace, a great musician and a great man. His name is best known today in connection with his famous *Dictionary of Music and Musicians.* The two struck up a warm friendship, and Grove became another very important convert to the Schumann music. Grove took a keen interest in young Sullivan, too, and though it was a hard and fast rule that only well-known composers were featured at the Crystal Palace Concerts, Grove broke the rule to let London hear Sullivan's *The Tempest,* at Easter in 1862. The young composer, eager to put his best foot forward, had completely rescored his work for this concert.

The Tempest justified Grove's faith. All London went wild over it. It had to be repeated the following week. Chorley, the critic, whose word was law in musical London, had only good things to say. Charles Dickens sought out Sullivan to say, ". . . I have been listening to a great work."

In its final form, Sullivan's music for *The Tempest* opened with an *Introduction* in which the fury of a violent storm is painted by the agitated notes of the *andante con moto.* For Act I of the play, he wrote an accompaniment for Ariel's song *Come unto these yellow sands,* music both delicate and uncanny, which merges with subtle art into *Full fathom five thy father lies.*

For Act II, the music accompanies the dialogue leading to Ariel's song *While you here do snoring lie.* In Act III are music for a *Prelude,* background music to provide an eerie atmosphere for the strange shapes bringing in the banquet, and a *Banquet Dance* as delicate as thistledown.

For Act IV, there is an *Overture;* music for Ceres' entrance; a duet, *Honor, riches, marriage blessing;* and music for the entrance of the nymphs and the dance of the nymphs and reapers. The rapid staccato notes of the dance give a spirited and merry touch to the dainty melody.

For Act V, there is a *Prelude* and music accompanying the dialogue leading to the song *Where the bee sucks.*

Though Sullivan's *The Tempest* frankly owes much to Mendelssohn, it is no slavish copy of another composer's style. Even in the dance for the nymphs and reapers, for example, where the Mendelssohn touch is most apparent, the orchestration shows individuality.

Atmosphere is obtained in ways peculiar to Sullivan's genius. His use of the woodwinds, for example, is his own. Sullivan always showed a preference for the reeds, and with them achieved some of his most charming effects. Throughout *The Tempest,* the composer displays his love of melody—gentle, smooth-flowing, deceptively simple melody. Harmonies are chosen with care, and are never allowed to offend by their flamboyance or strangeness. Above all, Sullivan exhibits in this music his ability to subordinate orchestral effects to the requirements of poetic sense, rhythm, and accent. Sometimes his orchestral commentary underlines the humor of a song, or lends atmosphere to a scene, but it never obtrudes aggressively. These are the qualities in his work which made him the ideal composer of opera.

Ariel's song to Gonzalo is an example of Sullivan's understanding of the dramatic in poetry. His music intensifies the mood of excitement and suspense suggested by the words:

If of life you keep a care, Shake off slum-ber and be-ware, A-wake!

On the strength of this success, Sullivan gave up the various teaching jobs with which he had kept body and soul together that first year out of school. "I hated teaching," he said, "and nothing on earth would ever have made me a good teacher." He accepted the post of organist at St. Michael's, Chester Square, and on the stipend he received for coaching the choir and playing the organ for services, he settled down to composing.

There is an amusing story about the choir at St. Michael's. Sullivan discovered that he was rich in soprano and contralto voices, but almost lacking in tenors and basses. There was a police station just around the corner; so the composer went visiting and recruited a dozen London "Bobbies" for his choir. "I used to think of them sometimes when I was composing the music for *The Pirates of Penzance,*" he said in later years, referring to the policeman's chorus in that opera.

Sullivan was making friends right and left. That wonderful singer whom he had worshipped from the audience when he was a chorister—Jenny Lind—invited him to spend the Christmas of 1862 with her and her husband, Otto Goldschmidt. Goldschmidt wrote, "We have been playing your *Tempest,* and Mrs. Goldschmidt has been repeatedly singing the pretty song and duet . . ." Fred Clay, who had studied with him for a while at Leipzig, knew all Bohemian London and introduced his handsome young composer friend to colorful groups of artists, musicians, actors, and authors. The Frederic Lehmanns became his intimate friends, the companions he liked best when in later and more prosperous years he traveled often to the Continent.

Toward the end of the year 1862, Sullivan was invited to accompany Chorley, Charles Dickens, and the Lehmanns to Paris. This was pure holiday, with the travelers following the energetic Dickens about from one restaurant and theater to another.

Sullivan met the aging Rossini, who played duets with him from *The Tempest* and otherwise showed his admiration for the young English composer. Rossini gave brilliant receptions. At one of these, he brought Carl Rosa over and introduced him to Sullivan. The two young men burst out laughing, for it seemed only yesterday that they had been students together at Leipzig.

Sullivan hurried home to be best man at his brother's wedding, and then settled down to his work. Dawn often found him still slaving over his music paper, but he was not slaving in vain. At twenty years of age he was already making his living with his art. Visiting his friend Grove at Sydenham, he met the beautiful daughter of one of the directors of the Crystal Palace and fell in love with her. All unaware that the wealthy parents of the girl had no intention of permitting her to marry a penniless musician of humble birth, Sullivan poured out his love in songs such as those he wrote in 1863–64. The five beautiful songs to words of Shakespeare belong to that period: *Orpheus With His Lute, O Mistress Mine, Sigh No More, Ladies, The Willow Song,* and *Rosalind.*

He was foolishly selling his songs to publishers for a lump sum. At Grove's suggestion, he ceased selling them outright. On the royalty basis, his income took a sharp turn upward.

In 1863, he composed two songs for English royalty—*Wedding March* for the Princess of Wales, and the song *Bride from the North* in honor of Alexandra. These pieces earned him the friendship of the Prince of Wales and the Duke of Edinburgh. The latter, a violinist of skill, remained throughout Sullivan's life his best friend.

After Fred's marriage, the elder Sullivans moved to Claverton Terrace, where Arthur went to stay with them for a time. They were a happy family. His mother was glad to be able to look after her son again, and cook his favorite dishes. His father was content to watch the boy's success, to encourage him with kindly, wise advice and affectionate pats on the shoulder. Not the least of Sullivan's assets was that of an understanding and loving family.

Sullivan was working at many projects during this experimental period. He composed a ballet, *L'Île Enchantée,* for Covent Garden. He wrote some music for an incredibly bad light-opera libretto by Chorley, *The Sapphire Necklace,* which was never produced. He spent the summer of 1863 in Ireland, where he worked on his *Symphony in E,* the "Irish" Symphony, which was not performed until 1866.

The cantata *Kenilworth, A Masque of the Days of Queen Elizabeth* was arranged from Scott's novel *Kenilworth.* Sullivan slaved over the libretto, another of Chorley's. The book was the most difficult he ever tried to set to music.

Though *Kenilworth* must inevitably suffer by comparison with Sullivan's later dramatic works, it was by no means the failure that a few critics have made it out to be. As a matter of fact, when the work was played at the Birmingham Festival in September, 1864, there was no mistaking the enthusiasm of the listeners, who sensed that this was merely a beginning for the talented composer.

Thomas Sullivan sat in the audience, happy and proud. This was one of the few public performances of his son's works that he ever heard, for in the fall of 1866 he died. The suddenness of his passing was a severe shock to the family. Arthur, who had adored his father, managed to keep calm before his grieving mother, but to friends he spoke of his loss and wept.

"Oh, it is so hard—it is so terribly hard—" he cried out in his anguish.

How desperately Arthur missed his father's calm words of encouragement perhaps only Fred knew. The older brother had been in the habit of dropping in evenings to smoke a pipe of tobacco with his father in the kitchen. Arthur, coming home from some late rehearsal, would find them there, smoking like chimneys and talking in low tones so as not to disturb Mrs. Sullivan. The composer's cares seemed to drop away from him in their serene company.

Both Fred and Thomas Sullivan knew that the youngest member of the family was greatly troubled in the years preceding *Kenilworth*. The nagging fear that all was not well with his romance gave way to certainty when the girl broke off the engagement. Arthur could not understand, could not accept the decision. He tried to keep his trouble to himself, but he could not conceal his restlessness. His music suffered. He had promised a composition for the Norwich Festival to be held in October, 1866, but there was no inspiration. His father patted his shoulder, and told him earnestly, "You musn't give it up. You will succeed if you stick to it."

Remembering those words, the composer began to write on the evening of his father's funeral. He was making a beginning with his Overture *In Memoriam*. In pouring out his grief and loneliness in this music, Sullivan found a measure of peace at last. The beautiful memorial to his father was his contribution to the Norwich Festival.

Time softens grief, and Sullivan was young. He came to accept the loss of his father, and thought very seldom of the girl he had loved. He was himself again when in 1867 Grove proposed an exciting adventure. Grove had reason to believe that there was much Schubert music in manuscript somewhere, possibly in the dusty cupboards of Viennese music publishers. He was particularly eager to discover the missing parts of the beautiful *Rosamunde* music, of which only fragments had come to light. Would Sullivan like to go with him to the Continent and make a search? The young composer's eyes sparkled. Would he! They wrote to Herr Spina, music publisher of Vienna, telling him of their purpose, and set off late in September like two explorers about to enter an unknown land.

They combined business with pleasure. Fred went with them as far as Paris, where they ate some good food, saw a few plays, and visited musical friends before going on to Baden. At Baden they visited Madame Schumann and Madame Viardot Garcia, and then went on to Salzburg, where Mozart had lived. They visited the famous Mozart museum, where Sullivan gazed reverently at the harpsichords, portraits, letters, and manuscript music belonging to the great composer whose genius he admired above all others.

They called on Herr Spina as soon as they arrived in Vienna. He produced some Schubert manuscripts, and gave them leave to copy as much as they wished of this "lost" music. He had nothing of *Rosamunde,* however.

Spina gave them an introduction to a Dr. Schneider, a relative of Schubert's, who had some of the composer's work. In a cupboard at this man's house, the two enthusiasts found the part books for the whole of the *Rosamunde* music. Covered with the dust of nearly half a century, these treasures had probably been "tied up after the second performance in December, 1823, and probably never disturbed since," Grove surmised.

Grove and Sullivan worked all night copying the precious music. When they had finished, and realized to the full that they had before them priceless music which the world had given up for lost, they began to play leapfrog. Dr. Schneider, who had already made up his mind that the two Englishmen were a little odd, would have been convinced that they were insane if he could have seen them. Two Victorian gentlemen in sideburns celebrating at dawn with a game of leapfrog must have been a funny sight.

Sullivan went from Vienna to Prague, and from there to Leipzig. The city of his student days turned out with enthusiasm to hear a performance of *In Memoriam* at the Gewandhaus. On the same program was the great Russian composer Anton Rubinstein, whom Sullivan had heard in the Chapel Royal days. Rubinstein played his own *Concerto in D minor*. After the performance, he went with Grove and Sullivan to dinner at a restaurant popular with the music crowd. Young Sullivan had come a long way since he was a boy chorister knocking timidly at the gates of music.

From Leipzig, Sullivan went on to Dresden. There he attended a performance of Wagner's *Rienzi,* which he criticized frankly as "very commonplace, vulgar, and uninteresting."

Returning to London by way of Paris and the Exposition, for which he had prepared some musical arrangements, Sullivan settled down once more to his composing. Among the eleven songs he turned out in 1867–68 were *The Long Day Closes* and a charming lullaby written for Fred's little son Herbert, *Oh, Hush Thee, My Babie.*

In 1867, the composer was elected to the Garrick Club, of which the English painter Millais was a distinguished member. These two became fast friends, and in later years Millais made a fine portrait of his composer friend. The painter was a man who could entertain his friends by the hour with anecdotes of the famous and interesting people with whom his work brought him in contact. Not the least interesting of the stories were his recollections of the genial Irish miniaturist, Samuel Lover, the grandfather of America's Victor Herbert.

Sullivan's first oratorio was *The Prodigal Son.* Dashed off at amazing speed, three weeks from beginning to end, it was produced at the Worcester Festival in 1869. Because of the poor singing of the artists taking part, this work was only the partial success that it became in later years with Sim Reeves singing the leading rôle. Sim Reeves made such a success of this part that he became identified with it. He once sent his portrit to Sullivan with the inscription "To Arthur, from his Prodigal Son."

Sullivan's first excursion into comic opera came about through a chance meeting with Burnand, the editor of *Punch.* A member of Burnand's staff had died, and the editor proposed to sponsor a benefit show for the man's family. He asked Sullivan to write something for an amateur performance. When the composer agreed, Burnand hastily adapted a farce called *Box and Cox,* by Morton, and presented Sullivan with a libretto which was named *Cox and Box.*

Sullivan had fun writing the music. At the benefit performance,

George du Maurier, artist and costume designer, later of *Trilby* fame, sang the lead, and Sullivan himself was at the piano. The audience went wild over the little burlesque, with its delightful lullaby *Hush-a-bye, bacon* and Box's hilarious description of his "suicide of convenience." Other performances were given. The piece made money. No one was more surprised than Sullivan.

On the strength of this success, he and Burnand wrote another operetta together. They called it *The Contrabandista,* and gave it to the German Reeds to produce. Because of a dismally inadequate cast, the work was a failure. Sullivan abandoned the idea of composing for the comic-opera stage. And then he met Gilbert.

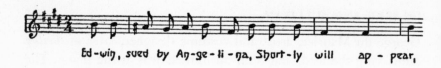

Ed-win, sued by An-ge-li-na, Short-ly will ap-pear,

3

TWO YEARS passed after the meeting in 1869 at the German Reeds before Gilbert and Sullivan were brought together as collaborators. In the interval, both men were busy.

Sullivan returned to serious music with the *Di Ballo Overture* for the Birmingham Festival of 1870 and the cantata *On Shore and Sea* written for the opening of the International Exhibition at South Kensington in 1871. Numerous songs and hymn tunes poured from him, and he worked at his music for Tennyson's *The Window; or, The Songs of the Wrens,* which gave him a certain prestige in the eyes of his Victorian contemporaries.

He made a trip to Paris after the Franco-Prussian War, and returned bewildered and hurt. Sullivan never had the least understanding of the soulless politics which lead to imperialistic wars. He thought only in terms of individual men and women. How German boys like those he had known in Leipzig could have been recruited to shell his beautiful Paris he could not understand. Why the French workers had rebelled against the fifth column in their own country and set up the Commune in those chaotic days was a mystery to him. What made the whole French people decide that they had had enough of kings, why they deposed the third Napoleon and set up a republic was a puzzle. He turned his back on the whole thing and fled back to his island home, where it seemed to him that everything was right as right could be. It gladdened his heart that his Queen requested a complete set of his works. He was the only composer, not even excepting the beloved Mendelssohn, to be so honored. After all, Sullivan was a Victorian too.

As for Gilbert, he was seeing his plays produced with amazing regularity. The Princess, a take-off on Tennyson's poem of the same name, and The Palace of Truth were successful productions in 1870. The very year of the first venture with Sullivan, 1871, he was the author of six plays, among them the highly profitable Pygmalion and Galatea, which is said to have earned him more than forty thousand pounds (nearly $200,000).

Some time during this period of hard work and gratifying success, Gilbert had casually presented a libretto to John Hollingshead. He had no preference as to a composer for his verses, but the manager of the Gaiety burlesques had a very definite idea. He went straight to Sullivan.

Sullivan was glad to turn his back on the distressing aftermath of war in Europe. He was also rather glad to escape the humdrum grind of serious music, in which he was beginning to suspect that he had advanced very little artistically since his Tempest music. It would be a relief to take up a light, gay work and think up jolly rhythms and tunes for it. He agreed to set Gilbert's libretto.

The traditional musical cries of London street vendors selling violets, cockles, or hot cross buns disturbed Sullivan, breaking in upon the melodies singing in his head. He decided to rent a cottage in the country, and found what he wanted at Widmore Farm in Bromley, Kent. In "a little old-fashioned cottage with a good deal of ground and surrounded by roses" he settled down contentedly. By the middle of July, 1871, he wrote a friend that he was "beginning to get some work done, which was quite impossible in London." What he was working on, of course, was the music for Gilbert's libretto *Thespis; or, The Gods Grown Old*.

At the end of the pleasant summer in Kent, the composer was back in London with the completed score. The cast assembled by John Hollingshead went immediately into rehearsal under Gilbert's direction. Sullivan coached the singers and supervised orchestral rehearsals, but took no part in the staging of the piece or the directing of the acting.

Watching his collaborator conducting this part of the work, he was filled with admiration. Gilbert took his job seriously. Nothing was left to chance. Both principals and chorus were drilled in diction, enunciation, and "stage business" in a way no burlesque director had ever drilled them before.

The playwright's insistence on perfection led, naturally, to friction with certain actors and actresses. These artists were promptly introduced to Gilbert's sharp-tongued scarcasms. During one of the rehearsals, while Gilbert was earnestly coaching the chorus, a singing actress taking one of the principal rôles protested to the director that she should not be made to stay on-stage.

"Really, Mr. Gilbert," she said in her haughtiest manner, with a contemptuous brief glance at the chorus. "Why should I stand here? I am not a chorus girl!"

"No," Gilbert replied, "your voice is not strong enough, or no doubt you would be."

Other temperamental members of the cast thought twice after

that before they exposed themselves to Gilbert's scathing and witty "dressing downs."

Sullivan's eyes danced with merriment during these scenes, because he also had a grievance against those Gaiety artists who tried to give themselves airs. In recalling the difficulties of staging *Thespis,* he once declared that in those early days "there were comparatively few actors or actresses who could sing, and of those who pretended to, hardly any could be said to compass more than six notes. Naturally I found myself rather restricted as a composer in having to write vocal music for people without voices!"

Sullivan had another reason for taking an interest in the rehearsals. His beloved brother, Fred, whose ability as an actor and singer had proved itself in amateur theatricals, was making his professional début in the rôle of Apollo in *Thespis.*

The operetta was offered as a Christmas treat at the Gaiety Theatre, opening on the evening of December 23rd, 1871. When the curtain rose on the first scene—the summit of Mount Olympus with shattered columns lying about an ivy-covered ruined temple —the burlesque audience was not sure whether this classic fare was to its taste or not. Some liked it, some did not. After a month, those who did not care for Gilbert's subtle wit or choruses that did not show their knees won the argument, and *Thespis* bowed off the boards. Musical-comedy audiences of the seventies were not yet ready for Gilbert and Sullivan.

As a matter of fact, *Thespis* was not a very strong beginning. The piece is much ado about nothing. The characters—Greek gods and goddesses of Olympus and a company of actors—are too remote from the realms of reality to be of much interest. The plot is neatly constructed, with some clever lines and a good song or two foreshadowing the Gilbert and Sullivan magic of the later operas; yet it leaves us cold and unresponsive at the end, with the feeling that Gilbert wrote aimlessly and at random. Very little of the music has survived, but what there is of it suggests that Sullivan was not inspired to write above the level of the mildly pleasant.

The story begins with the gods of Olympus. They are represented as aging deities who have let their temples go to ruin, and show themselves generally worn out and tired of the daily round as they go about their tasks. Mercury is the only one with any youthful enthusiasm; so the rest of the gods send him pretty frequently to do their work. Mercury has reached the point that he resents being a "celestial drudge," doing all the work while the others take the credit. His clever song in which he tells how he lights up the sun and "Phoebus Apollo gets thanked for it!", how he edits all the learned books, and "that donkey Minerva gets credited," has a recurring chorus with one of Gilbert's bitterest jibes at empty-headed aristocrats who receive the honors due humble men of brains:

> "Well, well, it's the way of the world,
>   And will be through all its futurity;
>   Though noodles are baroned and earled,
>   There's nothing for clever obscurity!"

Taunts such as this were soon to reach the ears of the English Court, and memory of them was stored away until the day when there would be devised "a punishment to fit the crime."

While the old gods and goddesses are complaining and blaming each other for various troubles, a group of actors is seen climbing up the mountain. They have been given a holiday by their manager, Thespis, to celebrate the betrothal of two of their com-

pany, Sparkeion and Nicemis, and have brought picnic baskets to
Olympus.

The gods are at first horrified to have their sacred grounds thus
invaded, but when they finally condescend to talk to the actors,
they find themselves telling their troubles and asking for suggestions. Thespis tells them that their main trouble is that they have
grown out of touch with the people of the earth, and suggests
that they go down and live amongst mortals for a time. The idea
both startles and fascinates the gods. Diana voices the general approval of the plan with some amusing lines:

> "I, as the modest moon with crescent bow,
>   Have always shown a light to nightly scandal,
> I must say I should like to go below,
>   And find out if the game is worth the candle!"

The gods raise one objection. If they go below, Olympus will
have no deities to carry on the tasks of lighting up the sun, polishing the moon, conducting wars, and so on. Thespis suggests that
his company, which is capable of playing new parts at a moment's
notice, carry on the duties of the absent gods for one year. So it
is agreed, and the actors divide up the various rôles amongst them.

But the actors run into serious difficulties. In another of his
sarcastic thrusts at the English ruling class, Gilbert says:

> "A premier in Downing Street, forming a Cabinet,
>   Couldn't find people less fit for their work!"

The thespians fall to quarreling. Jealousy divides them. Love
affairs get hopelessly entangled. They try experiments with sun,
wind, rain. About the only constructive thing they do is rebuild
the ruined temple.

When the gods return at last, they are wrathful over the way things have gone. The days have been jumbled, with Saturday losing out altogether. Fogs have been so misplaced that Athens has not had a sunny day for six months. And the grapes produce ginger beer instead of wine. In terrible anger, Jupiter and the other gods banish the inadequate players:

> "Away to earth, contemptible comedians,
>   And hear our curse, before we set you free;
> You shall all be eminent tragedians,
>   Whom no one ever goes to see!"

With those lines, Gilbert took his revenge on the actors and actresses who had made his own labors as director difficult.

His reference to "eminent tragedians" was a vicious thrust at certain famous actors of the day, particularly Sir Henry Irving, whom Gilbert always disliked to the point of hatred. Irving was an actor at the top of his profession, idolized by his public and praised to the skies by the critics. Probably all this popularity and adulation did tend to make him arrogant and contemptuous of the creative efforts of others. He would not be the first—or the last—great actor to allow his self-esteem to go beyond the bounds of good taste.

Irving once said that Gilbert was "a librettist who soared to write original comedy." Gilbert retaliated by giving an interview to the press in which he ridiculed the Shakespearean performances of Irving, declaring that the actor could not make a poetic speech of thirty lines interesting to the audience and that he mouthed his verse like an Eton or Harrow schoolboy on Speech Day.

Here and there in *Thespis* are touches which have the originality and topsy-turvy humor of the best of the *Bab Ballads* and the later Savoy operas. In the song about Hymen, the god of love who refuses to marry, there is such a "Gilbertian" touch:

> "He swears that Love's flame is the vilest of arsons,
>   And looks upon marriage as quite a mistake;
> Now, what in the world's to become of the parsons,
>   And what of the artist who sugars the cake?"

In those lines, one sees the extraordinary facility which Gilbert shows in his use of the feminine rhyme. This was a knack which gave the songs in his operas a swinging musical quality that made them a joy to his composer.

Gilbert's humorous choice of words coupled with clever rhyme is evident in his duet for Sparkeion and Nicemis:

Nice. "He's my husband, I declare,
        I espoused him properlee."
Spark. "That is true, for I was there,
        And I saw her marry me."

The lukewarm reception of *Thespis* did not encourage John Hollingshead. He made no further attempt to stimulate a joint work by Gilbert and Sullivan. Sullivan returned to his serious music. Gilbert went back to writing "straight" plays.

Only one song from the score was ever published—the delightful *Maid of Arcadee*. When asked the reason, Sullivan once said that he saved the score to borrow from for later works. It is well known that the rather commonplace air of Lady Blanche's song *In this college* from *Princess Ida* was taken from the music of *Thespis*.

Gilbert borrowed from *Thespis,* too. The whole first chorus of the actors, *Climbing over rocky mountain,* was used with a few minor changes as the first chorus of General Stanley's daughters in *The Pirates of Penzance.*

Four years passed before Gilbert and Sullivan came together again. Nothing in their private lives tended to draw them together, surely. Sullivan ran with princes and dukes; Gilbert made fun of aristocrats and shunned their society. Sullivan liked the bright, not-too-serious company of salons and drawing rooms; Gilbert preferred to have a few chosen friends for long week-ends at his home or aboard the yachts he was fond of sailing in coastal waters off Cornwall.

Shortly after the *Thespis* venture, Sullivan met a woman who was to have the profoundest influence on his future career. This was Mrs. Pierre Lorillard Ronalds of Boston, a beautiful woman and a singer of charm and ability. A friend of the deposed Napoleon III and Empress Eugenie, she had followed them from France to London. At their "court in exile" she had been introduced to the Prince of Wales, a fact which assured her an important place in English social circles.

Mrs. Ronalds quickly established her own "court" in London. She was a wealthy woman, able to indulge her whims. Everyone who was anyone came to the Salon at No. 7 Cadogan Place, pleased to be the guest of the woman who had thrown a spell even over Queen Victoria.

The Duke of Edinburgh brought Sullivan round to meet "the permanent ambassadress of the United States at the Court of St. James's." From that moment, Mrs. Ronalds became the composer's dearest friend and guiding spirit in all that he did. To the day of his death, hardly a day passed without his meeting Mrs. Ronalds or exchanging letters and telegrams with her.

If ever a time existed when Sullivan might have been tempted to withdraw from Society—the kind with a capital S—it was forgotten in Mrs. Ronalds' salon. His life led him more and more into ways of ease and pleasure, and the earnest young composer of *The Tempest,* in whom old musical friends like George Grove and George Macfarren never ceased to see the promise of symphonies and operas, gave way before the genial composer of light-opera tunes which filled his purse and allowed him to gamble at Monte Carlo, own race horses, and hobnob with royalty.

Perhaps it was just as well. There is considerable evidence, even in the best of his serious work, that Sullivan was not cut out for the larger forms. *The Tempest* is graceful, with a beauty which is that of the cameo rather than of the sculpture in marble. The churchly tunes of Sullivan's oratorios and sacred cantatas are piously devout, never religiously exalted. The composer sparkled most in the care-free atmosphere of light opera, and was no less an artist for it.

Many honors came to Sullivan in these four years. He was named conductor of the "Classical Nights" at Covent Garden Promenade Concerts, and was chosen to select musicians for a permanent orchestra for the Royal Aquarium at Westminster. He wrote a *Te Deum* to celebrate the recovery of the Prince of Wales from typhoid fever, a work which was produced at Crystal Palace with a chorus of hundreds of picked voices and an orchestra of two thousand musicians.

He wrote some charming music for *The Merchant of Venice,* and an oratorio, *The Light of the World,* which won him the honorary degree of Doctor of Music from the University of Cambridge. There was even talk of a knighthood.

He continued to write hymns, among them the well-known

Onward, Christian Soldiers. Then as if his Sabbath mood weighed too heavily on his spirits, he turned to lighter work. For John Hollingshead's production of *The Merry Wives of Windsor* he wrote some gay incidental music. He even experimented with a comic opera called *The Zoo.*

Meanwhile, Gilbert was making himself unpopular with princes and prime ministers. His play *The Happy Land* was produced in March, 1873. It was a satire on Gladstone and the English party system, and was promptly banned by the censor. The man who wrote

> "Poor Britannia
>   Although she rules the waves,
> Britons ever, ever, ever
>   Shall be slaves."

was likely to be more of a favorite with the man in the street than the guests at Mrs. Ronalds' salon. It is a wonder he and Sullivan ever did consent to get together. There must have been a touch of the rebel in Sullivan, too, to account for the partnership. Perhaps he never forgot that a snobbish caste system made it impossible for him to marry the girl he loved.

Gilbert's *The Happy Land* was followed by *Charity,* in which he called down on his head the wrath of the moralists of his day. Then he took a vacation from controversial themes with *On Bail, Topsy-Turveydom, Sweethearts, Tom Cobb,* and *Ought We to Visit Her?* These plays were successes, but *Broken Hearts* was an out-and-out failure. It took a year to write and played three months. Gilbert, who always believed that *Broken Hearts* was his best play, felt angered and frustrated. He, like Sullivan, was ready for a change of fare when in 1875 he was offered the chance to collaborate in writing another comic opera.

In 1875, a well-known actress of the day, Selina Delaro, was directing and appearing in a season of operas by the Frenchman Jacques Offenbach. A very remarkable man was doing an efficient job as her manager at the Royalty Theatre in Dean Street, Soho. This was Richard D'Oyly Carte.

Born in Soho in 1844, in the very neighborhood of the Royalty Theatre, he grew up in an atmosphere of music and the stage. His father, besides being a flutist of considerable ability, was a partner in a firm of manufacturers of musical instruments, Rudall, Carte & Co. Richard worked in the Rudall, Carte firm as instrument maker, studied music, and attended the University of London.

When he finished his college studies, he undertook to make composing a profession, but even though three of his operettas were produced and a number of his songs published, he lost interest in this vocation. He considered the idea of entering his father's firm. He toyed with the idea of becoming an actor.

Finally, he solved his problem by combining his talents in the career of theatrical manager. He opened a musical and dramatic agency, varying the business of booking tours for individual performers and companies with the management of London theaters. Carte's astute business sense, born of practical experience, together with his knowledge of what was good in music and popular in drama, soon made him the most successful agent and manager in his profession. Added to skill and experience were his shrewd ability to take the measure of those with whom he dealt, and a genial personality which made him the pleasant companion, friend, and co-worker of artists of most diverse temperaments.

He was just the man to bring about the permanent partnership of Gilbert and Sullivan.

Carte had never forgotten *Thespis*. While the rest of the Victorian world was busy remembering that Sullivan had composed *The Prodigal Son* and *The Light of the World*, Carte was remembering *Cox and Box*. When everyone else thought of Gilbert as the author of *Pygmalion and Galatea*, Carte remembered the *Bab Ballads* and *Ages Ago*.

When Miss Delaro ran into difficulties at the Royalty with Offenbach's *La Perichole*, which proved too short for an evening's entertainment, Carte saw an opportunity to carry out a pet project of his. He would fill out the evening with a short operetta written to order.

He mentioned the idea to Gilbert one day, and asked if he could supply a libretto on short notice. Gilbert replied that he could do better than that. He could supply one immediately. In his desk lay a libretto in manuscript, based on an early satire of his contributed to *Fun* in 1868.

When Carte read Gilbert's *Trial by Jury*, he knew that he had found what he wanted. Here was an English operetta, with an English subject, a little masterpiece of pungent satire and bubbling humor. Carte also knew the right composer for it. Sullivan. He lost no time in making an appointment for Gilbert to call on the composer.

The air was thick with swirling snow, and the English landscape was like a scene from one of Dicken's Christmas stories the day Gilbert put on a heavy overcoat and walked through the London streets to Sullivan's rooms in Albert Mansions. And this was all very right and proper, since the story in his pocket was a take-off on a breach-of-promise suit reminiscent of that hilarious case in Dickens's *Pickwick Papers* of Bardell v. Pickwick, from which it has been claimed Gilbert drew his inspiration.

When chairs had been drawn up before a blazing fire in Sullivan's comfortable parlor, Gilbert began to read. He seemed to be less and less pleased with his play as he went along, reading his witty verses as if they sounded to him very silly and beneath his dignity as a serious playwright. To Sullivan, however, the manuscript made an instant appeal. He found it funny from beginning to end. Though the perturbed Gilbert did not realize it, the composer was shaking with silent mirth throughout the reading.

Sullivan's appreciation of Gilbert's sparkling lampoon of an English court, where solemn be-wigged judge, jurors, attorneys, and court ushers all sang and danced their way through a suit brought by Angelina against Edwin, was all the more keen because of his friendship with the very proper Lord Chief Justice, Sir Alexander Cochrun. The idea of a man like Sir Alexander explaining in song how he came to be a judge, sending "mash notes" to the plaintiff, and dancing with the chorus of bridesmaids tickled his fancy. At the end of the reading, Sullivan reached for the manuscript. The great partnership was launched at last.

Within two weeks all of the music for this opera, which consumes about an hour's playing time, was composed and scored. In fact, the opera was written, rehearsed, and produced in just three weeks. It opened at the Royalty on March 25th, 1875, as an "afterpiece," but was soon promoted to "curtain-raiser."

Londoners who had paid their money to see and hear Offenbach's French opera were taken by surprise when the curtain went up on a familiar court scene. The set was a faithful copy of a courtroom in the Clerkenwell Session House, where Gilbert had practiced as a barrister.

Three outstanding artists took the principal parts. The judge was played by Fred Sullivan. Unlike many a later comedian interpreting the rôle, he did not try to clown his way through the part, but played it with all the dignity and gravity associated with the bench. He allowed Gilbert's comic words to speak for themselves. The result was very much as if a real judge in a real court, without throwing off his dignity of *manner,* had spoken his secret frivolous and unorthodox thoughts. Fred's performance brought down the house every night.

Nelly Bromley, a beautiful tall girl with a good voice, was the plaintiff, "the broken-hearted bride," and managed to be at once so lovely and so absurdly hypocritical with her weeping and flirting and pleading for damages that her admiring audiences were left weak from laughter. A young comedian playing his first rôle on the stage made a tremendous hit in the minor part of the Foreman of the Jury. This was W. S. Penley, of *Charley's Aunt* fame.

Trial by Jury set the pattern for a new type of comic opera, which came to maturity in the hands of Gilbert and Sullivan. The chorus, in this case the jurors and the bridesmaids, always had a logical place in the story, singing comments on the action of the play very much in the old Greek manner. The autobiographical song, which appeared in all the later operas, was introduced for the first time with the judge's comic ballad.

Sullivan's music was delightful throughout, from the opening solemn chords sung by the jurors, counsel and usher against a playful commentary in the orchestra to the final rollicking "For he is a judge, and a good judge, too." Like Mozart, whose fun-loving nature reveled in excursions into light comedy like *Cosi*

Fan Tutti, Sullivan combined thorough musicianship with humor, sympathy, and good taste.

And now for the play—

As the curtain rises on a court of justice, jurymen in their box, attorneys, and barristers are singing lustily

"Hark, the hour of ten is sounding"
and go on to state that "in this arena"

> "Summoned by a stern subpoena,
>   Edwin, sued by Angelina,
>   Shortly will appear."

The usher approaches the jury box. To a mock-serious accompaniment, in which the bassoon contributes just the right touch of the ridiculous, he advises the jury to set aside all prejudice in hearing the case.

> "With stern judicial frame of mind
> From bias free of every kind
>   This trial must be tried."

The jurymen chorus dutifully:

> "From bias free of every kind
>   This trial must be tried."

This slavish repetition of his warning annoys the usher, who sings very loudly during the chorus:

> "Silence in court!"

The jurors do subside, finally, and the usher goes on to instruct them how to act when the plaintiff presents her case. He suggests that as they listen to her story they

"Observe the features of her face—
The broken-hearted bride."

He tells them that they must "condole with her distress of mind,"
and then piously adds:

"From bias free of every kind
This trial must be tried!"

As for the defendant, the usher tells the jury that they need pay
no attention to him whatever. "What *he* may say you needn't
mind—" But of course

"From bias free of every kind
This trial must be tried!"

The jurymen, like the twelve good men and true that they are,
take this advice very seriously. When Edwin, the defendant,
enters, they shake their fists at him and shout:

"Monster, dread our damages.
We're the jury,
Dread our fury!"

Edwin, not unnaturally, is considerably dismayed at this reception, and pleads with the jury to listen, at least, to his side of the
story. Noticing that Edwin carries a guitar and will presumably
treat them to some music as he tells his story, the jury leave the
box and gather round him.

Edwin explains how it is that he came to jilt the fair Angelina.
It seems that he was madly in love with her at first, but as time
went on, he became bored with her and transferred his affections to another. Sullivan provided an absurd little tune for the

"Tink-a-tank-tink-a-tank" with which Edwin divides his song into stanzas.

The jurymen confess that they did the same thing when they were young, that they behaved like cads, in fact—but of course in their maturer years "that sort of thing is all over." Each one declares:

> "I'm now a respectable chap
>   And shine with a virtue resplendent
> And, therefore, I haven't a scrap
>   Of sympathy with the defendant!"

With that disquieting (to Edwin) sentiment, they dance back to the jury box, ending their song with a gay "Singing so merrily— Trial-la-law!"

The usher announces that the judge is about to enter. All rise and greet him with a song of churchly harmonies. The judge thanks jurors and attorneys for their kind reception, and suggests that before he hears the case, they might be interested in his own autobiography. The chorus is delighted, and says so. In this piece, Sullivan was having a hearty laugh at the tedious contrapuntal choral sections of serious oratorios and cantatas, such as Handel wrote, which he himself wrote, and which Victorian England at least pretended to enjoy.

There has seldom been such clever "kidding" of what is dull and lengthy as in the amusing

> "He'll tell us how, he'll tell us how,
>   He'll tell us how, he came to be a judge."

The words of the chorus rise, soar, sink to earth, rise soar, sink again. Each time they sink to rest, the audience is hopeful that it is for the last time. But no such luck. Just as they seem to have exhausted themselves, up they spring and rise to soar again, always harping on the same tune, a poor weak thing to begin with. To make the situation funnier still, the judge, anxious to tell the story of his life, tries time after time to break in, with

"Let me speak!"

But the chorus keeps right on singing, as if they did not hear,

"He'll tell us how, he'll tell us how."

With this fun at the expense of orthodox composers out of the way, the judge's song commences.

Whereas Sullivan's music takes the spotlight in the amusing chorus, Gilbert's words demand the center of the stage in this song. Sullivan, who realized the importance of giving each star his moment in the limelight, graciously yielded place. It has been said that with the musical accompaniment of this song and all those of its kind, Sullivan "did nothing in particular, and did it very well."

The judge tells the court how he began as a poverty-stricken barrister, who was starving for lack of cases when he found a way out of his troubles by marrying a rich attorney's "elderly, ugly daughter," of whom her father said,

"She may very well pass for forty-three
In the dusk, with a light behind her!"

After that, the rich attorney helped his son-in-law and

"The briefs came trooping gaily."

Once he was on his feet, financially, the judge confides that he threw over his ugly wife. This background being, as anyone can see, the ideal one for a judge of a breach-of-promise suit, he and the jurors sing:

"For now I (he) am (is) a judge!
And a good judge, too."

When the counsel for the plaintiff arrives, the usher swears in the jury. Again Sullivan had his little joke. The music for the ceremony has all the solemnity of a church service.

The usher raises his voice and calls lustily for the plaintiff!

"Oh, Angelina! Come thou into court!"

Outside, presumably in the corridors, the cry is echoed:

"Angelina! Angelina!"

Preceded by her bridesmaids, all in flowing gowns and flower garlands, the plaintiff enters in full bridal array, bouquet, veil, and all.

Angelina tells how broken-hearted she is. The jury are obviously captivated by the beauty of the bride and her attendants. The judge sends a note first to one of the bridesmaids and then orders it passed on to the bride.

Counsel for the plaintiff presents his case "with a sense of deep emotion," in a song with absurdly high-flown words. Meanwhile, the plaintiff acts out her part, pretending to faint, leaning first on the foreman of the jury and later on the shoulder of the judge himself.

Edwin does his best to plead his case, saying that change is nature's law, that no one blames the changeable weather, nor a man who, tiring of beef, turns to mutton. He ends his plea by saying,

"I'll marry this lady today,
    And I'll marry that lady tomorrow!"

The judge thinks this may be a way out, but counsel for the defense, after referring to a huge law book, declares that
"To marry two at once is Burglaree!"
The matter seems to have reached a deadlock. The plaintiff seizes on this moment of doubt and indecision to drive home her point, that she still adores Edwin. She throws herself into his arms, all the while calling the jury's attention to the "love and caressing" which she has lost when they are deciding
"The damages Edwin must pay!"
Edwin repels her furiously, painting himself as a blackguard who drinks to excess. He asks the jury to remember that he is not prepossessing when they are assessing
"The damages Edwin must pay!"
The jury is completely bewildered, and the judge takes a hand with:

"The question, gentlemen—is one of liquor;
    You ask for guidance—this is my reply:
    He says, when tipsy, he would thrash and kick her,
    Let's make him tipsy, gentlemen, and try!"

But the attorneys sing, "I do object!" In fact everyone but the defendant objects, and the court is in an uproar with "I do object; I don't object!"
The judge loses patience and tosses his books and papers about. Coming down from the bench to the floor of the court, he embraces Angelina and sings:

"Put your briefs upon the shelf,
I will marry her myself!"

This is a solution which pleases everyone, and the gay little opera closes with variations on the usher's song:

"It seems to me, sir,
Of such as she, sir,
A judge is he, sir,
And a good judge, too."

The English from very early days have loved and made their own simple songs, ballads, and dances with melodies as fresh as a May morning. Gilbert wrote the words and Sullivan the music for many a piece with the charming simplicity and seeming artlessness of the old English folk songs. One of these is *Comes the Broken Flower,* sung by the bridesmaids in *Trial by Jury:*

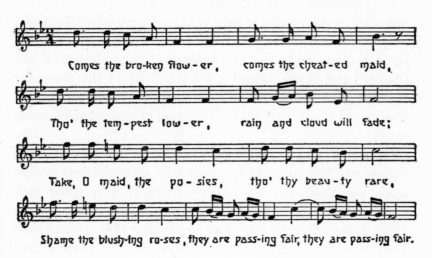

Comes the bro-ken flow-er, comes the cheat-ed maid,

Tho' the tem-pest low-er, rain and cloud will fade;

Take, O maid, the po-sies, tho' thy beau-ty rare,

Shame the blush-ing ro-ses, they are pass-ing fair, they are pass-ing fair.

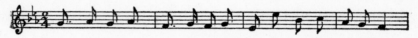

Let the air with joy be lad-en, Rend with songs the air a-bove,

4

ELL PLEASED with the success of *Trial by Jury,* Carte could not rest until he had commissioned a full-length operetta. He prepared an elaborate prospectus of a plan to produce all-English comic opera. With this he went first to several music publishers, later to men of business in other fields.

A good many months of hard work and persuasive talk passed before he was successful in forming the Comedy Opera Company, the financial backers of which were music publishers Frank Chappell and George Metzler, John Collard, of the pianoforte Collards, and Bailey-Generalli, known as "Watercart Bailey," who owned nearly all the water-carts used to sprinkle the London streets.

Carte was anxious about his proposed venture because both Gilbert and Sullivan were very busy with successful independent work, and there was a strong possibility of their going their separate ways. Gilbert and Fred Clay produced a money-making comic opera called *Princess Toto* in October 1876 at the Strand Theatre, which some years later was a huge success in the United States. For the production in the United States, Gilbert wrote into *Princess Toto* a parody of *Hiawatha* which tickled the funny bone of all America.

Sullivan, meanwhile, was accepting his Doctor of Music degree from Cambridge, and allowing himself to be persuaded by the Duke of Edinburgh to undertake the principalship of the National Training School of Music, which later became the Royal College of Music. In spite of a life-long dislike of teaching, Sullivan held this position for nearly six years.

Lewis Carroll did his best to persuade the composer to set his *Alice in Wonderland,* but fortunately for Carte's venture, the idea did not appeal to Sullivan. The composer may have been annoyed at Carroll's smug pretense of not understanding music, an attitude which seems to have been something of a fashion in Victorian times. Carroll actually wrote:

". . . what I know of your music is so delicious (they tell me I have not a musical ear, so my criticism is valueless, I fear) that I should like to secure something from you now . . ."

Many years later, in a speech made in the Town Hall, Birmingham, Sullivan had his say about the popular lofty scorn of music, which Carroll, whether he realized it or not, had in common with his contemporaries:

"I am not here to explain why music should be cultivated, nor to apologise to superior-minded persons for its existence, nor to speak humbly and with bated breath of its merits; but I claim for it boldly and proudly its place amongst the great things and the great influences in the world; and I can but express pity for those who are ignorant and stupid enough to deny its importance in the world and history, and to look upon it as a mere family pastime, fit only for women and children.

"... when any one assumes a tone of lofty superiority, and boasts that he knows nothing about music, and pretends not to be able to distinguish one tune from another, you may either accept his statement with a considerable amount of reserve, or conclude that there is something wrong in his physical or mental faculties, and recommend him to consult an artist."

With the necessary financial backing at last, Carte wasted no time in signing contracts with Gilbert and Sullivan for an opera, and leasing a theater. He chose the oddly situated little Opéra Comique, reached by staircases from Holywell Street and a long tunnel from the Strand.

While Carte assembled a cast, hired a musical director, and selected musicians for an orchestra, Gilbert set to work on his libretto. As in the case of *Trial by Jury,* he drew on one of his published stories, which had appeared in a Christmas number of *Graphic.* He called his opera *The Sorcerer; or, The Elixir of Love.*

Sullivan consulted enthusiastically with both Carte and Gilbert, helping in the selection of singers, making suggestions to improve the musical possibilities of Gilbert's book. All his love of life and gayety bubbled to the surface. He was almost impatient to begin the work of composing.

Then, quite without warning, Fred became ill, so ill that it was soon apparent that he would not rally. All thought of work was dismissed, and Sullivan in an agony of dread sat night after night beside his beloved brother. It seemed beyond belief that death could take Fred—Fred just thirty-seven years old, Fred who had made everyone laugh during the run of *Trial by Jury,* for whom Gilbert was writing the part of Dr. Daly in *The Sorcerer,* genial, warm-hearted Fred. But so it came about. Fred died on January 18th, 1877, and Sullivan was broken-hearted.

Only one composition came out of those sorrowful days. Once when Fred fell into peaceful slumber, Sullivan leaned back in his chair and closed his eyes wearily. He did not doze, but tried to think of something comforting, healing. Some verses he had read in *Household Words* came into his mind—a poem by Adelaide Proctor. On scraps of paper which lay at hand, Sullivan started to sketch a musical setting for the words. The finished composition was *The Lost Chord*. Written from beginning to end at the bed-side of his dying brother, it was a memorial to Fred, just as *In Memoriam* had been his tribute to his father eleven years before.

There are few songs which have achieved such fantastic success as *The Lost Chord*. Within a few months of its publication its sales numbered more than the sale of all the songs of England for forty years. Mrs. Ronalds introduced it to the brilliant musical circle which clustered about her. The Prince of Wales (later Edward VII) once declared that he would travel the length of his future kingdom to hear Mrs. Ronalds sing *The Lost Chord*. Many years later, the first phonograph recording played in England was of Mrs. Ronalds' voice singing this memorial song.

Rich and poor, musician and non-musician—all took *The Lost Chord* to their hearts and found comfort in the hymn-like music. It remains one of our best-known and best-loved songs.

There was no more music from Sullivan's pen for many months. Working on the care-free *Sorcerer* seemed out of the question. In late spring, however, Sullivan pulled himself together and began the first sketches. It was uphill work, particularly when it came to setting the Vicar's songs, which Fred would have sung. But like Mozart, to whom he often has been compared, Sullivan was able at length to rise above his personal troubles and write music as gay and sunny as his heart was sad.

Carte was assembling a remarkable cast. Both he and Gilbert knew that the old-style singing actors and actresses, brought up either in the tradition of French comic opera or Italian opera buffa, would not do. A new type of comic opera required new and pliable material.

The backers of the company were frankly amazed when Carte began to hire men and women with no professional stage experience. George Grossmith, who was a reporter by day and a drawing-room entertainer at private parties and Y.M.C.A. programs by night, was selected for the important rôle of John Wellington Wells, the Sorcerer. Grossmith had only a fair voice, but his enunciation was so good that even in the rapid patter songs he could be understood in the gallery, and he was a born comedian. Time was to prove what a fortunate choice he was. Probably no other actor associated with the Gilbert and Sullivan operas achieved his popularity. Sullivan once asked him jokingly how much he paid people passing him in the street to say, "Look! There's Grossmith!"

Grossmith himself was dubious about signing a contract with Carte. He had never appeared on the stage. To do so would make it impossible for him to go back to his life of "society entertainer." Certainly a Victorian Y.M.C.A. would have had no more to do with him. Theatrical people were considered as part of the "underworld" in those days. Decent Victorians could not invite them into their homes.

Grossmith expressed his doubts both to Carte and to Sullivan.

He would find himself out on a forked limb if he did not make a success of the part. Sullivan invited him to his flat for an audition. Striking a note on the piano, the composer requested Grossmith to sing and hold that note as long as possible. The singer threw himself into the effort to please. Sullivan looked up, his eyes twinkling, and said, "Beautiful!" Then the composer asked Grossmith if he thought he could sing the Sorcerer's rapid patter song, *Oh! my name is John Wellington Wells*. Grossmith was sure that he could.

"Then you can sing the rest," Sullivan assured him.

So it was that the odd-looking, nervous little man who had made a meager living as a "society clown" signed the contract which launched him on the way to becoming one of the most celebrated singing comedians of his day. He played all the clowning rôles from the Sorcerer to Jack Point.

Rutland Barrington was hired to play the part of the Vicar. He also was associated with the Gilbert and Sullivan operas for many years, playing the heavy, pompous Pooh-Bah, Major General, and Captain rôles to perfection.

Mrs. Howard Paul, an entertainer of semi-professional standing, was hired for the part of Lady Sangazure. She remained to play the elderly-lady rôles in many an opera to follow. George Bentham was recruited from Covent Garden, and Richard Temple from opera buffa. Without exception, they were singers who could act.

Carte made a point of hiring an all-English cast and chorus. This idea appealed to Sullivan, who felt strongly that English musicians seldom received a fair chance in their own country. He often remarked that England spent a great deal of money on Academies, Colleges, and Chapels where musicians were trained, only to throw them over in favor of foreigners when it came to hiring them professionally.

For his chorus, Carte selected as many singers as possible from the Royal Academy of Music. An amusing situation resulted. To overcome the prejudice against artists with Anglo-Saxon names, many English singers had adopted Italian stage names. All these names were hastily changed again when word went out that foreign names and pseudo-accents were no asset at the Opéra Comique.

Alfred Cellier, a fellow chorister of Sullivan's in the Chapel Royal days, was hired as musical director. Both Alfred Cellier and his brother, François, were associated with Gilbert and Sullivan opera to the very end, Alfred subordinating his own considerable talents as a composer to the work of interpreting Sullivan's music.

The pattern of the later Savoy organization was being designed. *The Sorcerer* and all the comic operas that followed it were written with a particular company in mind. Both Gilbert and Sullivan knew the limitations of their artists, and wrote and composed to bring out the best in each singer. Since the company changed but little through the years, at least where the major rôles were concerned, the characters in the operas became stereotyped. From *The Sorcerer* to *The Grand Duke* there were, almost without exception, an elderly woman of fading charms, and an elderly man who paired off with her at the last; the youthful lovers; a Vicar, Major General, Captain, or Pooh-Bah; a clown like John Wellington Wells, Ko-Ko, or Jack Point; and the chorus of villagers, sailors, daughters, pirates, and so on.

The operas were always cast and rehearsed by the author, composer, and manager. Sullivan supervised the musical auditions and orchestral rehearsals. Sitting at the piano, he accompanied and coached the singers in rehearsals. On the opening night, he conducted the orchestra. Afterward, Cellier took over.

Gilbert supervised every detail of costuming, stageset building, and the rehearsing of the cast in their lines and "business." His rehearsals were conducted separately from the music rehearsals.

Carte attended mainly to the business details. He interviewed artists, drew up contracts, ordered and approved costumes, sets, and stage properties, and attended to advertising and all other matters pertaining to the box office.

The curtain was rung up on *The Sorcerer* on November 17, 1877. Though the opera was, as one critic has put it, "little more than a collection of comic ideas mixed with a plot"—and that plot none too original—the work contained enough wit and sparkle to cause it to run for one hundred seventy-five nights. As for the music, it was not great, but it was adequate.

The Sorcerer was a decided financial success, and for that the world may well add its thanks to those of Carte, Gilbert and Sullivan. If it had failed, *H.M.S. Pinafore, The Mikado, The Gondoliers,* and all the rest of that jolly company might not have come to life.

The story of *The Sorcerer* is all about the engagement of Aline, lovely daughter of Lady Sangazure, to Alexis, son of Sir Marmaduke Pointdextre, and what happened between midday and midnight during the celebration of their betrothal. Sir Marmaduke is so pleased about the engagement that he has thrown his estate open to the villagers for the occasion. That his son has had the good sense to engage himself to marry a girl of ancient lineage makes the old man happy; that this girl is the daughter of the woman whom he himself secretly adores, has loved, in fact, since his youth, though he has never mentioned the fact to her, causes his cup to run over.

Among the villagers are Mrs. Partlett, a pew-opener, and her daughter Constance. As they stroll about Sir Marmaduke's gardens and lawns, Constance sighs and looks so woebegone that her mother demands to know the reason. Constance confesses that she is madly in love with Dr. Daly, the middle-aged Vicar of Ploverleigh, but that he remains unaware of her feeling toward him. Mrs. Partlett makes up her mind to play Cupid.

At that moment, unaware that he is observed, Dr. Daly wanders in pensive thought along one of the garden paths. The gentle Vicar, affected by the romance of the day, pauses in his walk and sings a ballad. This song with its familiar "Ah me, I was a pale young curate then!" has that delightful blend of graceful melody with flawless humorous rhyme which is the hallmark of Gilbert and Sullivan.

The Vicar is all graciousness and kindness when he sees Constance and her mother, but though the latter almost asks him outright if he loves her daughter, he is too much in the clouds to catch her meaning. During the dialogue, the orchestra plays a delicate little minuet in the Mozart manner.

Constance goes off weeping. The Vicar, puzzled and distressed, can only conclude that "she has something on her mind." He does notice, however, that she is a pretty little thing, and then takes himself sternly to task for his wayward thought.

Sir Marmaduke and Alexis come up to the Vicar, and there is an exchange of compliments in which Gilbert had his fun with old-world courtliness:

"May fortune bless you!" says the Vicar to young Alexis. "May the middle distance

"Of your young life be pleasant as the foreground—
The joyous foreground! and, when you have reached it,
May that which now is the far-off horizon
(But which will then become the middle distance),
In fruitful promise be exceeded only
By that which will have opened, in the meantime
Into a new and glorious horizon!"

That gives you an idea of Constance's beloved Vicar.

Promising Sir Marmaduke a carbon copy of this speech, the Vicar wanders away, followed by father and son in earnest conversation concerning what Sir Marmaduke thinks is a too-public display of affection on the part of young Alexis and Aline.

When the young lovers meet, sure enough they rush into each other's arms. Lady Sangazure and Sir Marmaduke long to do the same thing, but instead they preserve the old decorum of their youthful days. Their duet *Welcome joy, adieu to sadness!* is one of the charming moments of the opera, with its stately gavotte music.

The Notary, a dry-as-dust, shriveled little man, brings in the marriage contract, which is signed to the accompaniment of some pleasant but undistinguished music. When Alexis and Aline are alone, they discuss their deep love for each other, and wish that everyone in the village might love as they do. Alexis, it appears, has taken steps to accomplish this result. He reveals that John Wellington Wells of a firm of "family sorcerers" in St. Mary Axe has been invited to attend the fête. He is to administer a love potion to the guests, the idea being to bring about a state of universal love and happiness.

John Wellington Wells pops in, dressed in conventional top hat and frock coat. He sings the first of the Gilbert and Sullivan patter songs, which were to become an expected delight of Savoy-opera audiences. The music for this song employs the oboe for humorous comment, one of the few instances where Sullivan used this reed instrument as the orchestral clown. This is too often its rôle in the hands of less talented composers. Sullivan usually reserved this instrument for the delicate pastoral effects so well suited to it.

Wells, the Sorcerer, produces a vial of his love potion, which, in spite of Aline's misgivings, is put in the tea to be served the villagers. The Sorcerer explains that as soon as they have drunk the brew they will fall into a deep sleep. Upon waking, twelve hours later, each man will fall in love with the first woman he sees, and his love will be returned.

There is an incantation with appropriate weird music with which the Sorcerer raises the demon-servants of the god Ahrimanes and instructs them to make his love philter potent. As the spirits fly off with fiendish laughter, the villagers dance in to the delightful chorus, *Now to the banquet we press.* Gilbert, who was a master of diction and prided himself on using words precisely, took an Edwin Lear, Lewis Carroll delight in misplacing them for whimsical effect. This banquet chorus with its "rollicking bun" and "gay Sally Lunn" exhibits this very English brand of humor.

There follows the amusing *Tea-cup Brindisi,* with which the composer had his fun at the expense of the drinking song always to be found in Continental opera. The villagers drink their "pretty stiff jorum of tea," and fall insensible one by one as the potion takes effect.

Act Two takes place at midnight, when the villagers are begin-

ning to wake. The Sorcerer's potion does its work with a venge-
ance. Everyone falls in love with the wrong person. Constance,
who really loves the Vicar, has the ill luck to see the old Notary
when she wakes. She describes her state of mind, which is pretty
much the state of everyone's:

> "You're everything that I detest,
> But still I love you dearly!"

Sir Marmaduke feels an attachment for the lowly Mrs. Partlett.
To the Sorcerer's horror, Lady Sangazure falls in love with him.
Aline, who has drunk the potion at Alexis' insistence, dotes on
the Vicar. Alexis, seeing everything go wrong, is in despair.

One of Sullivan's happiest songs appears at this point. The
Vicar sings *Oh, my voice is sad and low*. In the interludes he plays
his flageolet, which is out of tune. Something about this performance brings a lump to the throat. In spite of the humor of the
verses and the grotesquerie of the Vicar's singing and playing,
Sullivan managed to impart pathos to the scene. One cannot help
thinking that there is a sigh and a tear for Fred's memory in this
music which he was to have sung.

Matters have become so hopelessly entangled that the only way
out is to reverse the spell. The only way to do this, John Wellington Wells reveals, is for the Sorcerer to sacrifice himself to the
demons of the god Ahrimanes. This he cheerfully agrees to do.
As he disappears amid fire and smoke, the spell is lifted and
everyone finds his true love. Alexis pairs off once more with Aline,
Sir Marmaduke with Lady Sangazure, Dr. Daly with Constance,
and Mrs. Partlett with the Notary.

The supernatural doings have whetted the appetites of the

guests. Sir Marmaduke invites everyone to a second feast, and
they troop merrily off to the tune of the rollicking bun and gay
Sally Lunn:

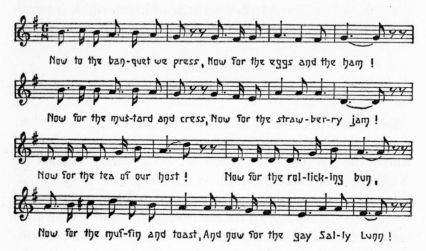

Now to the ban-quet we press, Now for the eggs and the ham !

Now for the mus-tard and cress, Now for the straw-ber-ry jam !

Now for the tea of our host !   Now for the rol-lick-ing bun,

Now for the muf-fin and toast, And now for the gay Sal-ly Lunn !

Nothing is more characteristic of the different temperaments
of the partners than their individual reactions to the success of
The Sorcerer. Both had had enough failures and partial successes
to be nervous about the outcome of this venture. When there was
no doubt that the opera was a "hit," Gilbert was so elated that he
sat down at once to write another libretto. Sullivan was so relieved that he went off to relax and enjoy himself. He went to
Paris.

While he was in the French capital, the composer conferred
with the Directors of the Paris Conservatoire. Sullivan had been
appointed Commissioner for Music for the forthcoming Paris
Exhibition. He was subsequently awarded the order of the Legion
of Honor in recognition of his services. The Conservatoire

honored him by playing his *In Memoriam,* the first time that the work of an Englishman had been performed at one of their concerts.

Before the end of the year, Gilbert had roughed out a story with a sea-faring background. He called it *H.M.S. Pinafore.* Sullivan returned from his Continental vacation and set himself the task of composing the music by spring.

No one would suspect, hearing the breezy score, that poor Sullivan was ill most of the time he worked on it. As early as 1872, the kidney trouble which was to grow steadily worse as the years rolled by put in its appearance. When he was composing the music for *Pinafore,* Sullivan was often doubled up with pain. During the worst attacks, he lay prostrate on a couch in his study. When the pain lessened, he rose weak and trembling and returned doggedly to his work.

The composer even found the energy to go to Portsmouth with Gilbert to study Lord Nelson's famous ship, *The Victory.* Through his friendship with certain officials of the Admiralty, the composer obtained permission for Gilbert to make sketches of the historic warship. From these sketches, a model was constructed and from this were made the plans for the ship set used in the opera. This stage ship was accurate, even to the smallest detail of its stays and gear. Gilbert saw to that.

Gilbert's meticulous regard for accuracy led to Rutland Barrington's making a bet with another player. Just before one of the rehearsals, Barrington had one of the ship's ropes wrongly placed, declaring that Gilbert's eagle eye would notice the error the minute he stepped on the stage. Barrington won the bet.

Sullivan, Gilbert, and Carte agreed on several new artists for the cast of *Pinafore.* The most important of these was Jessie Bond,

H.M.S. Pinafore

a youthful amateur who played Cousin Hebe in the first production of *Pinafore* and stayed for many years to become one of the most popular of the Savoy singers.

The Sorcerer had proved the value of Gilbert's type of directing. With *H.M.S. Pinafore* he carried still further his theory that the whole effect was more important than any single performance of a "star player." Gilbert demonstrated to his cast once and for all that his word was to be law.

He spent hours in his study working out the details of the action, using blocks of wood to represent the players. On a scale-model of the set, he moved his little dummy-players like chessmen. This one must move so many paces to the right when such and such a group came on. The group must form itself so when the soloist took his position at this particular point, and the soloist must move to that other particular spot when the chorus came on. With details worked out thus, he knew exactly what he wanted at the theater, and was in no mood to change his pictures to suit the temperament of a player with a different idea.

As in the case of *The Sorcerer,* there was friction. One temperamental actress insisted on standing at stage center when she sang. Gilbert ordered her to move to another spot.

"I come from Italian opera," she announced. "I always take the center of the stage for my aria."

"But this is not Italian opera," Gilbert pointed out, with that nasty edge to his voice that his players always dreaded. "This is merely burlesque of the lowest possible kind," he added sarcastically. The prima donna returned to Italian opera.

One of the leading male artists objected to being forced to stand for a long while during the rehearsal of minor parts.

"I have been on the stage long enough!" he said angrily.

"I agree," said Gilbert, and dismissed him from the cast.

Those were the days before actors' organizations, when a director could be a Czar and get away with it.

It took a good deal of fortitude and "knuckling under" to get along with Gilbert, who was sometimes unfair, often disagreeable, and always autocratic. Those players who managed to endure his temper and his bossing learned to shrug off his worst attacks by making little jokes behind his back. It was well known that Gilbert was over-fond of a candy called Almond Rock. Too much of it made him liverish and grouchy. His players spoke of those days when their director was particularly difficult as his Almond-Rock days.

Nevertheless, Gilbert was respected by the company, and liked too. He could be amiable and patient. He was known to spend hours drilling flustered amateurs, with never an unkind word for their nervous blundering. He expected his artists to work hard for perfection, but he set them the example of working harder still. The story is told that after hours spent drilling a chorus in a dance routine, Gilbert found the result anything but satisfactory. The performers were limp from their exertions, but Gilbert in a frenzy of energy leaped to the stage, showing the amazed chorus how the dance should be performed. It must have been funny to see him, a rather large Victorian gentleman with coat tails flying, leaping and pirouetting and shouting hoarsely:

"Ladies and gentlemen of the chorus, you must get this *right!*"

Incidents like this made the performers feel that Gilbert was one of them. The suave, pleasant Sullivan always remained an outsider. The actors respected him, but did not feel comfortable with him. In any difference of opinion concerning production, the performers invariably sided with their crusty director.

There was to be considerable trouble in store for *H.M.S. Pina-fore* before it settled down to become a popular favorite, but there was no indication of squalls ahead when the good ship got under way at the Opéra Comique on May 25th, 1878. All seats had been sold out days in advance, and huge crowds were turned away on opening night. From the moment Sullivan raised his baton for the Overture, an enthusiastic audience made it clear that this was to be one of the greatest of the Gilbert and Sullivan *premieres*.

There is plenty of salt in the opening chorus, sung by the crew of the *Pinafore* as they go about their work of splicing ropes, mending sail, swabbing the decks, and polishing the brass. The jaunty words

> "We sail the ocean blue
> And our saucy ship's a beauty"

set the mood for the whole opera.

The entrance of the hearty, not-so-young bumboat woman, with her basket of little delicacies and notions, is always greeted with laughter from the audience. Though it is traditional that she be made up to look as if she weighed three hundred pounds, she dances and flirts and hops about like a lass of sixteen summers. All this makes her introductory song, in which she calls herself "Sweet little Buttercup I!," funny indeed.

A modern audience finds little humor in the character of the sailor Dick Deadeye, whose deformed back Gilbert made sport of in the dialogue following Buttercup's song. The English audience of 1878 was not so sensitive on this point, however, and agreed with the hunchback's speech:

"From such a face and form as mine the noblest sentiments

sound like the black utterances of a depraved imagination. It is
human nature—I am resigned." If Gilbert was being ironical, the
point was lost on his audience. They knew Dick Deadeye for
the villain of the piece, and were ready to hiss him with
enjoyment.

Ralph Rackstraw, a handsome young sailor, was by virtue of
his youth and beauty sure to be the hero. To dispel any doubts,
he sang a plaintive *Madrigal* with the chorus. This was a Gilbertian take-off on the sentimental songs of Victorian drawing
rooms, with a deliberately sentimental tune by Sullivan. Following the last "Ah, well-a-day!," Ralph reveals why he is so sad.
In the charming *Ballad* he tells how he has the misfortune to love
his Captain's daughter. Because of his lowly station in life, there
is no hope for him.

While these revelations are being made, the bumboat woman
acts very strangely. She seems to be reproaching herself for some
past misdeed, and looks often at Ralph. "Ah!" thought Gilbert's
audience of 1878, well-trained in the ways of melodrama. There
had undoubtedly been dirty work at the crossroads, with handsome Ralph the innocent victim.

The Captain of the *Pinafore* enters the scene with the rollicking
song in which he declares: "And I'm never, never sick at sea!"
Probably no song that Gilbert wrote was so much quoted. The
crew's catechism of their commander and his replies took the
world by storm:

> "What, never?
> No, never!
> What, *never?*
> Hardly ever!"

It is said that this formula became so popular that the editor of a New York newspaper discovered to his dismay that in one issue his reporters had used it forty times. He issued orders that the first man to use it again would be dismissed from the staff.

To Buttercup, who, he remarks, is "A plump and pleasing person!" the Captain reveals that he, too, is sad. His daughter Josephine is sought in marriage by the First Lord of the Admiralty, but for some reason "She does not seem to tackle kindly to it."

Josephine enters sighing and singing a ballad to prove how

"Heavy the sorrow that bows the head
When love is alive and hope is dead!"

She tells her father that she cannot bring herself to love the First Lord, because she had already given her heart to one of the sailors. However, she assures her father that nothing will come of this attachment. After all, she remembers that she is socially above a "common sailor." Gilbert was taking a poke at the English aristocracy, which was already faced with the uncomfortable dilemma of trying to maintain class distinctions and at the same time appearing to support the growing demand for democracy.

Sir Joseph's approach to the ship is announced by a languorous barcarolle in Sullivan's most graceful style, a perfect foil for Gilbert's tongue-in-cheek words. The chorus of sailors offers the First Lord a hearty welcome. Sir Joseph enters the scene surrounded by a large number of female relatives, who endorse everything the First Lord says with "And so do his sisters, and his cousins, and his aunts!"

The audience at the Opéra Comique hailed the entrance of Sir Joseph with howls of delight. Word had got around that he was

a take-off on England's actual First Lord of the Admiralty, William
A. Smith, a publisher who had been appointed by Prime Minister
Disraeli to head the British Navy. Disraeli actually began to call
this Cabinet member "Pinafore Smith." Smith must have had
many an uncomfortable moment because of the famous comic
song sung by Sir Joseph, *When I was a lad I served a term*.
Sullivan gave this song a setting suggestive of a sailors' hornpipe,
a touch which pointed up the humor of the First Lord's autobiographical ballad.

The composer wrote a real hornpipe for the *Glee,* a song which
Sir Joseph brings with him in manuscript. He mentions the fact
that it is his own composition, and recommends that the crew
learn it. The manner in which Sullivan suggests that Ralph, the
Boatswain, and the Boatswain's Mate, who try to sing the song,
are not very good at sight reading is in itself humorous. He might
have had the three singers read the music off faultlessly, but instead he lets Ralph and the Boatswain falter now and then. The
Boatswain's Mate is the best musician of the three, for he carries
on when the other two can utter only broken fragments of song.

The crew joins in the chorus of the song as they get the hang of
it. All but Ralph dance off to the tune of Sir Joseph's bombastic
A British tar is a soaring soul. Ralph waits for Josephine to come
on deck. Plucking up courage, he tells her of his love, but she
spurns his advances and retires once more to the cabin.

A purely Gilbertian touch is provided by the entrance of Cousin
Hebe, the sisters and aunts, and the members of the crew. They
can hardly wait to find out how Ralph's suit is progressing. Their
sympathies lie wholly with the poor sailor. Dick Deadeye alone
is a cynic, taunting them with "She spurns you all—I told you so!"

With Dick Deadeye, Gilbert succeeded in painting a good

portrait of a man who believes in nothing and hates everything. Obviously, Dick is contemptuous of class distinctions, but he is equally contemptuous of those who seek to level the barriers. He is a defeatist. He turns out to be an informer, as well, disloyal to his forecastle mates. He is a very nasty man. Gilbert had a way every once in a while of injecting a serious note in the midst of the fun.

Ralph declares that life is not worth living, and the Boatswain obligingly hands him a pistol. The playwright was making fun of the "I die for love" type of literature of his day.

Josephine arrives just in time to stay her lover's hand by declaring her love. The sailors and the relatives join her in ecstatic song, *Oh joy, oh rapture unforeseen.* Dick Deadeye is the only wet blanket. When the lovers plot with the crew and relatives to steal ashore and be married secretly, he warns them that the match will be forbidden. The others brush him aside with *Let's give three cheers for the sailor's bride,* and the act ends with a spirited hornpipe.

Act Two begins with a really beautiful serenade. The Captain's *Fair moon, to thee I sing* is a typical Gilbert and Sullivan combination of poetic words of farcical meaning set to a graceful tune with genuine emotional appeal.

Buttercup joins the Captain as he finishes his serenade with

> "Say, why is everything
> Either at sixes or at sevens?"

She hints mysteriously that a great change is in store for him, in her song *Things are seldom what they seem.*

The Captain is not able to make head or tail of her jargon,

though he gathers that she wishes him well. The entrance of Sir
Joseph serves to take his mind off the riddle, however. Sir Joseph,
annoyed by Josephine's indifference, proposes that the match be
called off, but the Captain, eager to ally his daughter with a
Cabinet member, begs the First Lord to be patient. He suggests that Josephine may be shy because of her inferior social
station.

When they leave, Josephine comes on deck and sings a delightful parody of the Italian opera style in *The hours creep on apace*.
Having analyzed the step she plans to take in curiously impartial
fashion, contrasting her father's home with the poor home Ralph
will be able to give her, she pleads:

> "Oh, god of love, and god of reason, say,
> Which of you twain shall my poor heart obey!"

At this point, Sir Joseph joins her, and argues eloquently that
love should ignore class barriers, little dreaming that he is pleading his rival's case. The Captain comes on deck in time to join
them in the merry trio that begins:

> "Never mind the why and wherefore,
> Love can level ranks, and therefore,"

Just as the Captain thinks that everything is not quite so much
at sixes and sevens as before, Dick Deadeye brings him the shock-
ing news of the proposed elopement. Their duet shows the composer's profound understanding of voices and part writing. When
the two voices join in the refrain "Sing hey, the cat-o'-nine-tails
and the tar," they blend in pleasing harmony seldom obtained in
writing for two male voices in duet.

Carefully on tiptoe stealing is a bit of Gilbertian topsy-turvy-dom, for it is always sung with reckless volume by Josephine, Ralph, and the chorus, who are softly stealing away. The Captain appears dramatically, demanding of his daughter where she may be going "with these sons of the brine."

Ralph stands up to him, demanding that *he* be accorded the respect due an English sailor; and the chorus backs him up with:

> "He is an Englishman!
> For he himself has said it,
> And it's greatly to his credit,
> That he is an Englishman."

Gilbert the patriotic Briton was making merry with the false jingo patriotism which he could not endure, and Sullivan seized on the opportunity to write a tune that sounded like a national anthem. There is real nobility and grandeur in the musical setting for Gilbert's burlesque of narrow nationalism. An enthusiastic admirer of Gilbert and Sullivan once declared that this tune might with profit to all concerned be substituted for *God Save the King* as the National Anthem of Great Britain.

These democratic sentiments annoy the Captain to the point that he says, "Damme!" The horrified Sir Joseph immediately sends him below, and is about to pay some pretty compliments to Ralph, the noble sailor, when he learns the truth about the elopement. Ralph is promptly sent to a "dungeon cell."

Buttercup decides that the time has come for her to speak out. She confesses how "a many years ago" she took care of young babies. Two infants, one of "low condition," the other "upper crust" were entrusted to her, and she mixed them up. Ralph was the high-born babe, the Captain was the other. This means only one thing, that the Captain and Ralph must change places, caste being one of those inflexible things not subject to change, says playwright Gilbert mockingly.

Nothing could be better. Josephine's problem is solved. She is not marrying a penniless sailor, but a prosperous sea captain. Sir Joseph offers no objection, since it would be unthinkable for him to stoop lower than a captain's daughter, and Josephine's father has turned out to be nothing but a common sailor. As for the Captain, he is now lowly enough to marry the plump and pleasing Buttercup. They all sing their gratitude to the catchiest tunes of the opera, which ends with a resounding *For he is an Englishman*

After the first night, the ticket sales fell off. Carte knew that it was the unusually hot summer nights that accounted for the small houses, but the directors of the company, who were not theatrical men, blamed the opera itself. At least six times they put up notices that the play would be withdrawn, only to take the notices down again when the attendance increased. The cast could hardly sing because of the worry cause by these erratic proceedings.

Meanwhile, *Pinafore* was taking America by storm. There was no international copyright. Anyone could buy a printed libretto and piano arrangement of the music, provide a make-shift score, and start making money. Eight houses playing *Pinafore* were filled every night in New York, and at least forty companies were playing it in other parts of the United States.

News of the popularity of the work in America revived interest in the play in London. About the same time, Sullivan had the inspiration to do a little free advertising. He was still conducting at Covent Garden. On one of his programs he included an arrangement of the *Pinafore* music made by Hamilton Clarke. The success of *Pinafore* was no longer in doubt. It ran for seven hundred nights.

During those seven hundred nights, the history of *Pinafore* was a comic opera in itself. As soon as the directors saw that the piece was going to make money, they forgot all their previous doubts. Carte, however, remembered, and made up his mind to dissolve the company as soon as their lease expired at the end of July 1879. He gave his partners notice, and then set sail for America to see what could be done about the pirated versions.

When the fateful July night arrived, the directors decided to seize the scenery and stage properties and put the opera on at another theater. They sent a gang of muscle men back stage during the final performance at the Opéra Comique. The audience enjoying the gay music and bright dialog of the opera were suddenly treated to a very unmusical tumult from behind the scenes. The roughs who had come to dismantle the stage were confronted by the enraged singers and stage hands, and a free-for-all fight ensued.

Little Grossmith rushed out before the hastily drawn curtain when it became certain that the audience thought a fire had broken out and was about to stampede. He told them frankly what was happening. The situation struck the audience as funny. They roared with laughter. The sporting instincts of an English crowd were roused. All stayed to cheer the players, who came out of the fight victorious and finished the opera.

The directors did not give up, however. They had new sets made and hired a cast to present their version of the opera in the theater nearest the Opéra Comique. London chuckled over the fight, and went to see both versions. When the novelty wore off, Londoners turned thumbs down on the directors' show, and sealed with their approval the success of the partnership of Gilbert, Sullivan, and Carte which was about to be formed.

The experiment of an all-children cast for matinées was tried, and proved as popular as the evening show. The only person in London who objected was prim Lewis Carroll, who almost fainted when he heard the "big, big D" uttered by children.

Carte's researches in America convinced him that the only way for the author and composer of *Pinafore* to share in the profits of their work in the United States was to present an authentic version. This Gilbert and Sullivan agreed to do. Making the voyage on the Cunard steamship *Bothnia,* they arrived in New York November 5th, 1879, and immediately set to work to rehearse a cast. Fred Clay and Alfred Cellier were on hand to help with the novel venture.

They opened on December 1st at the Fifth Avenue Theatre, as the ninth company in New York. The first night was brilliant, but even curious New Yorkers eager to see the real *Pinafore* could hardly be expected to keep going year in and year out to the same comic opera.

Gilbert and Sullivan had expected something of the sort. They were armed with another opera, the music for which Sullivan completed at his lodgings on East 20th Street in New York. This was *The Pirates of Penzance; or, The Slave of Duty.*

While Sullivan was feverishly composing music for the pirate opera, London and America were singing, humming, and whistling a naive little waltz song, *I'm Called Little Buttercup.* As different from the voluptuous waltzes of Strauss as an English tea shop from a German beer garden, this is one of those ingenuous

pieces of Gilbert and Sullivan that refused, in spite of extreme
simplicity, to become monotonous.

I'm called lit-tle But-ter-cup, Dear lit-tle But-ter-cup,

Though I could nev-er tell why; But still I'm called But-ter-cup,

Poor lit-tle But-ter-cup, Sweet lit-tle But-ter-cup

With cat-like tread   Up-on our prey   we   steal .

 T A PRESS interview on their arrival in the United States, both Gilbert and Sullivan had some interesting remarks to make about their methods of writing, composing, and collaborating. Answering a question as to how it was his words were so closely wedded to the musical idea, Gilbert said:

"We have been working together harmoniously for the last seven years, and have learned to understand each other so thoroughly that even the faintest suggestion of the one meets with a ready and sympathetic response from the other."

Sullivan denied that his music was all inspiration without perspiration:

"Oh, it's a great mistake to suppose that the music of an opera bubbles up like a spring. We have to dig for music like the miner for his gold. It won't do for the miner to expect the gold to come up spontaneously. He has to dig deep for it, and so we, also, have to dig for our musical treasures."

The interview was printed in the New York Herald. The reporter added his own impressions of the two artists. Of Sullivan he said:

"In his appearance, gentle feeling and tender emotion are as strongly expressed as cold, glittering, keen-edged intellect is in that of Mr. Gilbert." It is one thing to be intelligent, quite another, to be "cold and glittering." Gilbert probably resented the comparison. All during the New York stay, he made a point of chaffing Sullivan unmercifully. Sullivan confided to Fred Clay that the witty but cruel barbs were more than he could bear. Seeds of future discord were being sowed.

With *The Pirates of Penzance* Gilbert and Sullivan and Carte determined to beat the American producer-pirates at their own game. A carefully selected cast, able to keep a secret, were rehearsed in New York. None of the music could be printed, because of the American copyright law then in force. This law permitted anyone to perform a printed work without paying author or composer, but interpreted the performance of a work in manuscript as theft. During rehearsals and the entire run of the piece, the manuscript music was collected from the orchestra and locked in a safe each night.

The music for most of this opera was written in New York, during the summer and fall of 1879. Before leaving England, Sullivan had written the songs for Act Two, and had sketched out most of the songs of Act One. In the hurry and excitement of leaving for America, the composer had neglected to take his sketches along. With only a month in which to work, and the steamship travel in those days very slow, there was no time to send for them. Sullivan rolled up his sleeves and did one of his impossible stunts. He rewrote all the songs of Act One from memory, completed the orchestration for both acts, and scored the entire opera—all in one month.

As a matter of fact, there was not much difference in the man-

ner in which this opera was written and rehearsed from all the
rest of the Gilbert and Sullivan productions. The method was
established very early. When the libretto was completed, Gilbert
called the entire company together, including Sullivan and the
musicians of the orchestra, and read them the book. Then Sullivan
began to set the songs for the second act, on the theory that the
best should come last, and should be written while he was fresh.
This was a sound theory. An audience requires time to "warm
up" to a performance. At the beginning, time is needed for getting
settled comfortably, adjusting wraps, and getting the names of
the cast of characters firmly in mind. If the play or operetta is
weak at this point, no one notices. Later, when attention has
been riveted on the plot and full interest roused, the songs and
dialogue had better be tuneful and clever.

Sullivan gave his songs for Act Two to the singers, who learned
and rehearsed them, and then began to compose the songs for
Act One. The composer supervised the song rehearsals, providing
the singers with a "faked" piano accompaniment. If Gilbert
suggested cuts or additons, to fit dramatic requirements, these
were made and the new versions rehearsed.

The spoken lines, stage business, dances—all were being perfected during the time Sullivan was composing. The scoring was
left to the very last minute, in case there were extensive changes
demanded by Gilbert. The overture was composed the last of all,
usually given to the orchestra the night or afternoon before the
opening performance.

This may have seemed to some of the artists an odd way of
doing things. The singers sometimes learned words and music
of their songs without having the slightest idea of where they fit
into the story. As for the orchestra, they practically had to play

the music at sight. The finished score was never ready for them before the dress rehearsal, and after this, major changes were often made. It was a nerve-wracking way to get an operetta together, demanding professional artists of keen intelligence and superior talent. Because of the high standard of artistry required, the Gilbert and Sullivan operas nearly always went off with the precision of clock-work on the night of the *Premiere*.

For *The Pirates of Penzance* matters were complicated by the necessity for secret rehearsals and the decision to keep the music in manuscript. All the parts for orchestra and singers had to be copied laboriously by hand. Gilbert and Fred Clay helped Sullivan with the labor of copying as time grew short, and Alfred Cellier assisted with the scoring. Even so, it is a miracle that so much was done in so short a time, and that the result was anything but a pot-boiler. In addition to getting the opera in shape, Sullivan had to help with the *Pinafore* production, and he accepted every dinner and speaking invitation extended to him. Both he and Gilbert felt that it was their duty to agitate for an international copyright law. They seized every opportunity to get their ideas before the American public.

The Pirates of Penzance does show the weaknesses of hurried work. Many of the tunes are commonplace. Others, not bad in themselves, nevertheless lack the facility and taste expected of the composer of *H.M.S. Pinafore*. But we cannot forget that in this opera occur the songs *Oh, better far to live and die, Ah, leave me not to pine, When a felon's not engaged in his employment,* and *Sighing softly to the river,* which rank with Sullivan's best later work.

When he wrote the libretto of *The Pirates of Penzance,* Gilbert's heart still lay with the sea and the success of his *Pinafore*. The

The Pirates of Penzance

curtain rises on a rocky shore on the coast of Cornwall, with a schooner lying at anchor in a calm bay. Groups of pirates lie about at their ease, some drinking, some playing cards. Their opening song is not quite so robust or rollicking as one would expect of a pirate band, but pleasant all the same:

> "Pour, oh, pour the pirate sherry;
> Fill, oh, fill the pirate glass;
> And, to make us more than merry,
> Let the pirate bumper pass."

They are celebrating the twenty-first birthday of their apprentice, Frederic, who is congratulated even by the fierce Pirate King. He is hailed as a "full-blown member of our band."

With regret, Frederic reveals that, far from intending to become a "master pirate," he plans to leave them forever. Pressed by his astounded companions for an explanation, he says that he may not tell them his reason for fear of hurting his former nursemaid, Ruth. Ruth, overhearing his speech, comes forward and makes the explanation herself.

It seems that when Frederic was a little lad, his father asked the nursemaid to take him and apprentice him to a *pilot*. Being hard of hearing, and not a little stupid, she mistook the word for *pirate*. Rather than face the boy's father when she learned her mistake, she decided to join the pirate band, too, as a "piratical maid of all work."

Frederic reveals that although he loves his pirate friends *individually*, as a group he detests them and will dedicate himself to their extermination. A sense of duty has bound him for twenty-one years, but at last he is free to devote himself to another sense

of duty. He is the *slave* of duty, in fact. This state of mind seems no
stranger to Gilbert's absurd pirates than the story Ruth has
told them. What is more, they are not even surprised when Ruth
confesses that, in spite of the difference in their ages, she loves
Frederic and would become his wife.

Ruth is a homely, silly, elderly woman trying to look like
seventeen. She gets on everyone's nerves. The pirates make no
secret of the fact that Frederic is welcome to take her with him,
but Frederic, who has never seen another woman, hesitates. Instinct warns him that there may be lovelier and younger women
in the world, in spite of Ruth's assurances that she is very beautiful
indeed.

When Frederic suggests that his pirate friends give up their
profession and return to the work-a-day world, the King declines
with thanks. He gives his reasons in a song which probably cost
Gilbert his knighthood in Queen Victoria's time:

> "When I sally forth to seek my prey
> I help myself in a royal way:
> I sink a few more ships, it's true,
> Then a well-bred monarch ought to do;
> But many a king on a first-class throne,
> If he wants to call his crown his own,
> Must manage somehow to get through
> More dirty work than ever I do,
>   Though I am a Pirate King."

The pirates go off, leaving Ruth pleading with Frederic to take
her with him. Suddenly the voices of young girls are heard. They
are the daughters of Major-General Stanley, come to wade in the

surf. As soon as Frederic sees these young beauties, he knows for
sure that Ruth has been deceiving him and denounces her. The
duet which follows contains some of Gilbert's cruelest thrusts at
aging femininity. Frederic jeers:

"Your face is lined, your hair is grey."
Ruth replies:
"It's gradually got so."

And though Ruth is, of course, a stupid, grotesque person, one
would rather not have met her at all than have had her pilloried
so mercilessly in her despairing last plea:

"Master, master, do not leave me!
    Hear me, ere you go!
  My love without reflecting,
  Oh, do not be rejecting.
Take a maiden tender—her affection raw and green,
    At very highest rating,
    Has been accumulating
Summers seventeen—summers seventeen.
    Don't, beloved master,
    Crush me with disaster.
What is such a dower to the dower I have here?
    My love unabating
    Has been accumulating
Forty-seven year!"

There is evidence that Sullivan disliked this kind of thing, too.
With the exception of the music provided for a similar aging lady

in *The Mikado,* his tunes for these despairing love-lorn females of Gilbert's is uninspired.

The girls, unaware of Frederic, who hides in a cave, dance and skip along the seashore, singing several pretty tunes, beginning with the song borrowed from *Thespis.* They begin to take off their shoes, which in Victorian times was the same thing as undressing completely. Frederic, being a gentleman, cries out that they are observed, and shows himself at once. The girls are startled and fascinated, too, at seeing him in his pirate's garb. When he tells them his story, they are all sympathy, crying out:

"How pitiful his tale!"

and by way of comment aside: "How rare his beauty!"

Frederic, finding himself in the midst of an admiring audience, proceeds to paint an even more pathetic picture of his "unfortunate position" then the facts warrant, and asks if there is not one maiden amongst them who will marry and reform him. The maidens promptly answer, "No, no—not one!"

One other sister, however, comes upon the scene belatedly and cries, "Yes, one!" This is Mabel, for whom Gilbert provided the tender lyric, *Poor wandering one!* Sullivan's music for this song is delicate and sentimental.

Mabel's sisters tactfully go apart from the lovers and try not to hear what they are saying. Sullivan's setting for *Yes, yes, let's talk about the weather* is deft and humorous.

Just as Frederic is warning the girls that it is not safe to remain so near the pirate hang-out, the buccaneers swoop down on them and are about to carry them off when the Major-General, their father, appears. He proceeds to tell the pirates just what kind of

Major-General he is, in one of Gilbert's funniest satiric songs. Sullivan, with his usual good taste, keeps the music entirely in the background, so that the words may be heard to their best advantage. Certain English army officers promoted because of family connections rather than ability found it hard to appreciate the caustic lines:

> "For my military knowledge, though I'm plucky and
>   adventury,
>   Has only been brought down to the beginning of the
>   century;
>   But still in matters vegetable, animal, and mineral,
>   I am the very model of a modern Major-General."

The wit and tomfoolery of this song are Gilbert at the top of his form.

> "About binomial theorum I'm teeming with a lot o' news—
>   With many cheerful facts about the square of the
>   hypotenuse."

would make even a stuffy professor of mathematics smile. And Gilbert and Sullivan fans appreciate:

> "Then I can hum a fugue of which I've heard the music's
>   din afore,
>   And whistle all the airs from that infernal nonsense
>   *Pinafore.*"

Following this nonsense, the General demands to know what is going on. When he learns the truth, he tries to think of some trick with which to thwart the pirates. He remembers that the pirates have a rule never to molest an orphan; so he tells them that he is a "lonely orphan boy," whose only comfort is his daughters. The pirates promptly release the girls, excusing their soft-heartedness with the whimsical

"For what, we ask, is life

Without a touch of Poetry in it?"

The act closes with the gay tune about the "doctor of divinity" who "resides in this vicinity."

Act Two takes place in a ruined chapel. Gothic windows show up eerily in the wan moonlight. In the chapel, General Stanley sits with sadly drooping shoulders. His daughters, all in demure nightdresses and nightcaps, surround him and sing *Oh, dry the glistening tear.*

Mabel begs him to tell them why he has left his bed "when happy daylight is dead."

Frederic enters and adds his entreaties to those of the girls, General Stanley finally confesses that his conscience bothers him. It was not true, his statement to the pirates that he is an orphan, and he explains that he comes to the chapel night after night to beg pardon of his ancestors, whom he had dishonored by this falsehood. The dialogue that follows is a stinging Gilbertian thrust at the "new rich," the social climbers whom he disliked almost as much as he did the true aristocracy.

Frederic: "But you forgot, sir, you only bought the property a year ago, and the stucco in your baronial hall is scarcely dry.

General: "Frederic, in this chapel are ancestors: you cannot deny that. With the estate, I bought the chapel and its contents. I don't know whose ancestors they *were*, but I know whose ancestors they *are*, and I shudder to think that their descendant by purchase (if I may so describe myself) should have brought disgrace upon what, I have no doubt, was an unstained escutcheon."

Frederic tries to comfort the General by telling him that the men he deceived are all black-hearted scoundrels, not worthy of being dealt with honorably. It is Frederic's intention to wipe them out that very night. He is to be accompanied by an armed guard of policemen. In full uniform and carrying dark lanterns, the "Bobbies" march in to the best song in the opera. The words are a take-off on the martial ballads of the *Scots wham Bruce has aften led* sort, with Sullivan's music pointing up the humor and giving it a background air that struts comically.

In this song, the girls tell the men that even though they die, their memories will be glorious and they will live in song and story. The men declare:

"We observe too great a stress,
  On the risks that on us press,
  And of reference a lack
  To our chance of coming back."

Still, they try to take a generous view with

"For it's very evident
  These attentions are well meant."

The absurd "Tarantara!" is sung loudly by the men to keep their courage up, for, as they themselves put it, when your heart is in your boots,

"There is nothing brings it round,
Tarantara! Tarantara!
Like the trumpet's martial sound,
Tarantara! Tarantara!"

The policemen march out, but before Frederic can follow, the Pirate King and Ruth sneak up and cover him with a pistol. There follows some typical Gilbertian nonsense, with Frederic acting as though, in spite of the pistol, he has the King and Ruth at his mercy.

Sullivan provided a rollicking laughing song for the paradox which the pirate couple reveal to Frederic. It seems that he was born in leap year on February 29th. His indenture papers read that he is to stay with the pirate band until his twenty-first birthday, not his twenty-first year. Therefore, he is still bound to them for many years to come. Frederic, being a "slave of duty" bows to this unanswerable logic and agrees to call off his private war against them.

When Mabel joins him, poor Frederic has to tell her what turn events have taken, and Mabel, also being a slave of duty, agrees that there is no alternative. He must go back to his pirate comrades.

After this broad farce, there comes a ballad sung first by Mabel then by Frederic. This is one of those moments of true sentiment and beauty in the midst of light farce, which Gilbert and Sullivan audiences came to expect eagerly. There is something which touches the heart in the beautiful harmony of the two voices singing:

"He loves thee—he is gone.
Fa-la, fa-la, fa-la."

Sullivan provided a winsome tune for the ensemble, *Oh, here is love, and here is truth.*

Frederic goes, and Mabel, almost fainting, tries to explain what has taken place. The policemen agree that, though they do not relish the idea, they must meet the pirates alone. The Sergeant and chorus then sing the famous *When a felon's not engaged in his employment,* with the two-line refrain which barber-shop quartets were soon rendering gleefully:

"Ah, take one consideration with another—with another,
A policeman's lot is not a happy one."

The pirates are heard singing in the distance. The comments of the police, who have hidden themselves, form a kind of response to the pirates' chant-like song. A clever plot situation becomes hilarious.

The boisterous *Come, friends who plough the sea* is a tune known to Americans as *Hail, hail, the gang's all here!* It is a disputed point whether Sullivan composed this tune; or whether he heard it as he walked through New York's Bowery. Whatever the truth, the song is now as American as corn on the cob.

The Major-General in dressing gown wanders in singing mournfully *tormented with the anguish dread* during which he says:

"And as I lay in bed awake
I thought I heard a noise."

There is a loud "Ha, ha!" from the pirates at this, but the old man seems not to hear and concludes:

> "It must have been
> The sighing of the breeze."

To a rippling orchestral accompaniment, the Major-General sings a truly lovely song, quaint in words and rhyme, dainty as a cameo in tune:

> "Sighing softly to the river
> Comes the loving breeze,
> Setting nature all a-quiver,
> Rustling through the trees—
> Through the trees."

His daughters, all carrying lighted candles, join him, and this is the moment for the pirates' attack. The policemen do their best, but are overcome. However, they have one last defense. The pirates are standing over them with drawn swords, but the policemen charge them to yield in "Queen Victoria's name." The pirates do so at once, declaring that "with all our faults, we love our Queen." The Major-General is about to send them all away for trial, when Ruth reveals that the pirates are all noblemen gone wrong. This fact gets them an immediate pardon and a present of the beautiful daughters of Major-General Stanley as well. "Because, with all our faults, we love our House of Peers."

Gilbert was having his usual jest at social inequality, and his thrusts went home. The year that Sullivan was knighted, Gilbert was conspicuous for his absence among the honored. When a command performance of *The Gondoliers* was given many years later at Windsor Palace, Gilbert's name was not even printed in the program. Queen Victoria had her own way of expressing dis-

pleasure with the man who ridiculed the hereditary members of
the House of Lords, and who wrote impudently of kings and
queens.

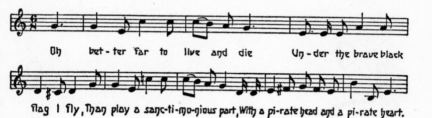

Oh   bet - ter far to   live   and   die   Un - der the brave black

flag I fly, Than play a sanc-ti-mo-nious part, With a pi-rate head and a pi-rate heart.

Why, what a ver-y sin-gu-lar-ly deep young man this deep young man must be !

6

BOTH GILBERT and Sullivan occupied themselves with a serious work on their return from America. It was nothing unusual for Sullivan to alternate tunes for heartiest burlesque with reverent church music. Having accepted a commission to compose a religious drama for the Festival of Leeds in 1880, he turned his attention from pirates to a poem by Dean Millman, *The Martyr of Antioch*. Finding that the poem was not ideally suited for musical setting, he asked, of all people, Gilbert to recast it. The surprising thing is that Gilbert accepted at once.

He, too, was able to forget the topsy-turvy humor and robust nonsense of his pirates and turn his attention to poetry of a higher order. The libretto he produced almost, if not quite, justified the high opinion he held of his abilities as a serious poet and dramatist, and he was enormously proud of his association with Sullivan in one of the sacred pieces.

The Martyr of Antioch was an immediate success. Of all Sullivan's religious works, it has stood the test of time best. Even in this field, Gilbert proved that he was the librettist best equipped to inspire the composer's genius. The experiment was never repeated, probably to Gilbert's regret. In a letter to Sullivan, he spoke graciously of the success which "will endure until music itself shall die," and added in all sincerity, "Pray believe that of the many substantial advantages that have resulted to me from our association, this last is, and always will be, the most highly prized."

With the praise of his *Martyr* music still singing sweetly in his ears, Sullivan packed his bags and went to Nice to spend Christmas. With him he carried part of a new comic libretto by Gilbert—*Patience; or, Bunthorne's Bride.*

Gilbert had turned once more to his *Bab Ballads* for inspiration. Choosing one of the wittiest, *The Rival Curates,* he outlined a plot in which parsons were held up to ridicule. In the ballad a parson is described thus:

> "He plays the airy flute,
>   And looks depressed and blighted.
>   Doves around him toot,
>   And lambkins dance delighted."

Gilbert always disliked these men of the church, and had lampooned them often in his contributions to *Fun.* The main reason for his scorn, it seems, was that women had a weakness for the "depressed and blighted" parsons. Being a hearty, robust, masculine sort himself, it hurt his vanity to see the meek, timid, soft-spoken "pale young curates" receiving the adulation and motherly attentions which he felt were more deserved by men of sterner stripe.

His attitude was so well known that once, when he was staying in a little town where a church conference was being held, he was recognized by the parsons at his inn, and one of them remarked with mild irony, "You must feel rather out of place in this company, Mr. Gilbert."

"Yes," .nswered the playwright, "I feel like a lion in a den of Daniels."

Before he had gone very far with his satire, however, Gilbert remembered *The Sorcerer*. The shocked surprise of people like Lewis Carroll, the author of *Alice in Wonderland*, at the spectacle of a comic vicar on the stage made him uncertain how a whole opera about comic churchmen would be accepted. Carroll in an article called *The Stage and the Spirit of Reverence* had written:

"Mr. Gilbert seems to have a craze for making bishops and clergymen contemptible. Yet are they behind other professions in such things as earnestness, and hard work, and devotion of life to the call of duty? That clever song, 'The Pale Young Curate,' with its charming music, is to me simply painful."

A hurried conference with Sullivan, whose every instinct was against lampooning churchly affairs, convinced Gilbert that he should abandon this plot. He turned back to an earlier idea, that of satirizing the long-haired poets of the aesthetic craze.

All England was familiar with Oscar Wilde, Algernon Charles Swinburne, William Morris, and others who led the back-to-the-Middle-Ages movement. Theirs was in reality a revolt against the dull frumpery of Victoria's England, which divided the country into two artistic camps. There were those who imitated the posing, the mystic talk, the eccentric dress of the aesthetes, and there were those who laughed at them or turned away in annoyance. There were, to Gilbert's disgust, a good many romance-starved women among the disciples. He himself belonged to those who scoffed.

The aesthetes of the eighties had already been satirized extensively. Oscar Wilde, at the youthful age of twenty-five, was better

known in the streets of London than the Prime Minister. Numerous witty articles had been written about his knee breeches, his
blue china, his poppies and lilies, which he carried with such an
air. One play in which he was unmistakably the central character
had set all London to laughing. Gilbert decided that it would be
much safer to fall in line and write his new piece about Wilde
and Swinburne than to vent his spleen against the clergy.

Taking the portly, posturing Wilde and the diminutive, affected
Swinburne for his models, Gilbert constructed a story which,
strange to say, achieved a timeless rather than a topical appeal.
Long after the "aestheticism" of the poems was forgotten as a
movement, Gilbert's opera excited laughter with its satire on
that trait in human nature which always provides bizarre prophets
with bizarre disciples.

The modern audience substitutes for the poets of *Patience* their
own "pet peeves," whether these be cultists with strange Eastern
or Ancient-Egyptian pseudo-philosophies, dull intellectuals talking endlessly about nothing, or "arty" people who draw, paint,
compose, or write "in terms too deep for *me*." In short, *Patience*
holds up to ridicule all who speak in cant phrases and pose for
the benefit of blindly adoring followers.

Sullivan took a look now and then at the manuscript which
he carried with him, first to the Riviera and from there to Italy,
but he was in vacation mood, and could not get down to serious
composing. At the end of January, 1881, he had done little or
nothing with the opera, but was enjoying himself thoroughly in
Paris, dining at Bignon's on the Avenue de l'Opéra, going to see
a play called *Divorçons* which was the rage of Paris, and accepting
numerous invitations from the musicians who lived in the gay
French capital.

The lawsuit which he and Gilbert and Carte had decided to bring against the directors of the Comedy Opera Company for their brazen theft of *Pinafore* called him back to London. There was no time for composing during the weeks in February and March when Gilbert and Sullivan and Carte were meeting almost every day in their solicitors' offices to discuss the details of the suit. The case went to court on March 10th, with nearly every prominent artist and manager connected with the theater present as witnesses or spectators. The Comedy Opera Company lost and were enjoined from performing the work of Gilbert and Sullivan, who were henceforth free to work out the terms of a contract with Carte. In all the operas that followed, the three shared equally in the costs and the profits of their work.

In addition to this worrisome legal business, Sullivan had been busy with rehearsals of his *The Martyr of Antioch* at the National School of Music. With the successful public performance at Albert Hall early in April out of the way, the composer took up the task of completing *Patience*. And it was high time. The opera was scheduled to open on April 23rd. By the 13th, Sullivan had sketched out all the songs and was already rehearsing the singers, but had not begun the scoring. In the amazingly short time of ten days, he scored the entire opera, including the overture.

Opening night for *Patience* at the Opéra Comique was a brilliant one. This was no accident. The smooth-running organization, which was to become the envy of other managers, accounted for it. Gilbert had given his usual careful attention to details of costuming and set design. His exacting rehearsals had perfected the cast in the smallest details of speech and business. By this time, most of the singers were old hands, quick to learn Sullivan's music as he wanted it sung. His patient coaching brought out the best in them. As for the members of the orchestra, under Alfred Cellier's direction they could play a score with feeling and understanding on very short notice. Teamwork was the keynote of the success of the Gilbert and Sullivan operas.

Whenever a new singer was engaged for an opera, he had to pass a rigid test. When Carte and Sullivan agreed that the new voice measured up to the general standard, Gilbert had to be satisfied that the artist's appearance was right for the rôle he would play. Gilbert did not care twopence if a newcomer could act. It was his theory that actors were made, not born, and that Gilbert was the man to make them.

An amusing story is told which throws light on the effective but informal way new talent was tried out. Walter Browne was selected by Carte to sing the rôle of Colonel Calverly in *Patience,* and was told to go to Carte's office to wait for Sullivan, who would hear his songs and make the final decision. Browne was very nervous. He arrived early for the try-out, and spoke of his doubts and fears to a man who was sitting in Carte's office strumming the piano.

"So you've come to sing for Sullivan?" said the man at the keyboard. "Well, for your sake, I hope you're in good voice. Best thing you can do is try over your songs with me before he gets here."

Browne gave the stranger his music sheets and sang through all his songs. When he had done, Carte walked into the office.

"Hello, Sullivan," he said to the man at the piano.

The audience reading the program at the Opéra Comique had an idea of what was up before the curtain rose on *Patience.* The

Officers of the Dragoon Guards were just the sort of lusty military men whom Gilbert would back in a contest with parsons or poets. Reginald Bunthorne, a "fleshly poet," was a caricature of Oscar Wilde. Archibald Grosvenor, an idyllic poet, was a take-off on Swinburne. This news had been whispered about during rehearsals. Grossmith and Barrington copied the mannerisms of the two poets too well for there to be any doubt about it after opening night. The chorus of "rapturous maidens" was Gilbert's revenge on all the adoring ladies who preferred vicars and poets to heartier men. Patience, a dairy maid, was the embodiment of wholesome, every-day English girlhood, to match the breeziness and sanity of the Heavy Dragoons.

The opening notes of Sullivan's music in the Overture set the tone of gentle melancholy and longing which characterize the love-sick maidens. In aesthetic Greek draperies, they group themselves artistically before the drawbridge to Poet Bunthorne's castle and sing plaintively to the accompaniment of lutes, mandolins, harps, and other "aesthetic" instruments.

Some of the more robust tunes of the opera are hurried through, and then the prelude of the opening chorus prepares the audience for the truly beautiful *Twenty love-sick maidens we*. The maidens reveal that their hopeless love for Bunthorne has reduced them all to "miserie," since he pays no attention to them. Gilbert's words jeer at these romantic, unhappy ladies, but Sullivan's music has compassion and understanding.

Lady Jane, one of Gilbert's aging ladies, enters and sadly informs her younger companions that they have been blind to the fact that Bunthorne is in love. The excited maidens ask who has caught his fancy, and Lady Jane replies that it is Patience, the village milkmaid. They try not to believe it, reminding each other that Patience has often said she does not know what it means to love.

Patience herself comes upon the scene, and stands for a moment regarding the love-lorn ladies with pity. Her dainty song, *I cannot tell what this love may be*, is Gilbert in his mood of combined humor and seriousness. Sullivan wrote a delicate pastoral melody with the artful simplicity of Early English music.

Patience tells the ladies that the 35th Dragoon Guards are on their way to see them, and is astounded when the etherealized maidens announce airily that though they were engaged to these military men the year before, they have since transferred their affections to the poet. They move off in procession to sing their morning carol for Bunthorne, and Patience, much puzzled, goes her way.

The Dragoons enter to the brisk chorus *The soldiers of our Queen*. The Colonel marches in, splendid in his uniform, to sing the lusty patter song which begins:

"If you want a receipt for that popular mystery,
    Known to the world as a Heavy Dragoon."

Bunthorne, completely absorbed in composing a poem, comes from his castle, followed by his adoring female admirers, who sing sadly:

"In doleful train
    Two and two we walk all day—"

The Dragoons watch this spectacle with growing amazement, and sing their spirited *"Now is not this ridiculous—and is not this preposterous?"*

While the maidens beg the poet to take notice of them, he remarks aside that, though he pretends not to hear them,

"Like a literary man
    Who despises female clay
    I hear plainly all they say,
    Twenty love-sick maidens they!"

He allows himself to be persuaded to read his poem. Gilbert's
lampoon of some of the weird, meaningless stuff passed off as
poetry is called *Oh, Hollow! Hollow! Hollow!* It is priceless
fun.

The Dragoons are taken aback when the ladies find fault even
with their uniforms. The followers of the poet are offended by
the vulgar primary colors. Lady Jane describes her idea of what
their uniform might be were it to conform to aesthetic prin-
ciples:

". . . there *is* a cobwebby grey velvet, with a tender bloom like
cold gravy, which, made Florentine fourteenth-century, trimmed
with Venetian leather, and Spanish altar lace, and surmounted
with something Japanese—it matters not what—would at least be
Early English!"

Stunned by this speech, the Guards watch the ladies go off. The
Colonel finds his voice to sing one of the best songs of the opera.
Sullivan proved that he could write music of masculine vigor.
One cannot listen to the music for *When I first put this uniform
on* without remembering that Sullivan in his youth played every
instrument in his father's military band.

When the Dragoons go off, Bunthorne sneaks in, and in a clever
recitative and song, confesses that he is a sham, that all his posing
is "Born of a morbid love of admiration!" Sullivan heightened the

humorous effect of these words by giving the orchestra agitated chords to illustrate the poet's increasing excitement.

With a cynicism which is as astounding as his strange costume and posturings, Bunthorne tells the audience just what they must do if they wish to shine "in the high aesthetic line as a man of culture rare." The poet's song of self-analysis is a gem of Gilbertian humor and rhyme. Everyone knew who was meant when Bunthorne said, "If you walk down Piccadilly with a poppy or a lily in your mediaeval hand." Even Oscar Wilde must have squirmed at the fun at his expense when Bunthorne confided:

> "And every one will say,
> As you walk your flowery way,
> If he's content with a vegetable love which would certainly
>   not suit *me*,
> Why, what a most particularly pure young man this pure
>   young man must be!"

Patience enters, and Bunthorne begins to tell her how much he loves her. Poor Patience is thoroughly frightened at his extravagant manner and speech, and is convinced that he is a maniac when he floats out quoting his own poetry, a little thing called *Heart Foam*, in which he speaks of a place

> "Where the dust of an earthly today
> Is the earth of a dusty tomorrow!"

Angela, one of the love-lorn ladies, enters, and Patience asks her to tell her two things: ". . . what on earth is this love that upsets everybody; and secondly, how is it to be distinguished from insanity?"

Angela explains that it is a pure and unselfish emotion, that everyone should experience it, that it is a *duty* to fall in love. Patience bursts into tears, blaming herself bitterly for having been so selfish all her life. Angela leaves her with her sore conscience.

Patience is talking to herself, declaring that she will make it a point to fall in love, when Poet Grosvenor enters. Stranger though he appears to be, he immediately sings a courting song to Patience. Of all the songs written to resemble folk songs (and there are many graceful ones in Gilbert and Sullivan) this is undoubtedly the most winsome. It has a strange antique air which suggests a kinship with old Irish music. Gilbert's words are "frolicsome and free," with a puckish humor all the more mischievous because of the wistful tune. The simplicity and symmetry of the setting recall Mozart's genius. Sullivan, like Mozart, could write music so disarmingly simple that it seemed to sing itself. Those who would imitate a song like *Prithee, pretty maiden—prithee, tell me true,* however, find that more art is required to create the illusion of artlessness than ever goes in to the writing of a heavy, pedantic work.

Grosvenor reveals to Patience that he is not a stranger, after all, but her childhood sweetheart. He complains that his rare beauty is his chief sorrow, for it causes every woman he sees to fall in love with him. Patience is no exception, but on learning how perfect this poet is, she decides that to love him would be a selfish act— and Angela has convinced her that it is a duty to love unselfishly, that is to say unhappily. This is the aesthetic creed, and poor simple Patience accepts it, being, as it seems, like Frederic of piratical fame, a slave of duty.

The long *finale* to Act One contains a number of good tunes, beginning with the classic music for the maidens as they lead Poet Bunthorne off to be raffled for. The chorus of Dragoons, in which they demand of the poet what he has done to be led about like a sacrificial ox bound with garlands of roses, is a delightful bit of gay music wedded to nimble verses:

"Then tell us, we pray you,
  Why thus they array you—
  Oh, poet, how say you—
    What is it you've done?"

Just as Lady Jane reaches into a bag to draw the first ticket, Patience cries, "Hold!" She announces that she is ready to accept the poet in marriage. Bunthorne shouts joyfully that she loves him, but the little dairy maid sets him straight in her tuneful song *True love must single-hearted be,* to which Bunthorne responds at the end of each line, "Exactly so!"

Realizing that the poet is lost to them forever, the aesthetic ladies turn to the Dragoons and embrace them during the *Sextette, I hear the soft note of the echoing voice.* This is nothing more or less than a hymn tune. Sullivan, who often wrote this kind of music in dead earnest, realized that some of it was pretty bad, and indulged in a little self-parody now and then.

Just as the military men seem to have won the field, Poet Grosvenor enters. The ladies are at once fascinated by his "god-like grace." When in answer to their questions he admits, "Yes, yes—I am aesthetic," they cry rapturously, "Then we love you!"

The act closes with a skillful setting for all voices in which the chorus of girls, Dragoons, Patience, Grosvenor, and Bunthorne speak their different private thoughts to the same tune. Grosvenor is in distress, Bunthorne is jealous of his popularity, Patience is unhappy, the girls are wild with joy, and the Dragoons comment, "Now is not this ridiculous!" Which, of course, it decidedly is.

The second act opens with a recitative and song by Lady Jane, who accompanies herself on a mediaeval double-bass. If the aesthetic maidens were travestied before, they are surely laughed to scorn in this scene. Gilbert's malicious words in the song *Silvered is the raven hair* would be unbearable bad manners if it were not for Sullivan's music. This is not the first time he had softened the crudities Gilbert seemed to delight in, nor would it be the last. Whatever he may have thought of his task—and there is ample evidence that he did not relish it—Sullivan did his job of "glossing over" very well. His absurd passages for Lady Jane's bass fiddle, coming as they do after she has sung a line of recitative unaccompanied, prove something that Sullivan denied in theory, that music in and of itself can be funny. But this humor is not Gilbert's brand. Gilbert grabbed Folly by the scruff of the neck and called out indignantly for all passers-by to observe the spectacle; Sullivan threw Folly a whimsical glance and passed by with amused or pitying smile.

Of all the rapturous maidens, Lady Jane alone has remained faithful to Bunthorne. She feels sure that he will tire of Patience. Meanwhile, the others sit at the feet of Poet Grosvenor, who is persuaded to read some of his poetry. His verses are particularly unpoetical; yet the maidens have nothing but praise for them. Poor Grosvenor, stifled by all this unwanted attention, begs the girls to give him the usual commercial half-holiday. He tells them that he can never return their love. The graceful *A magnet hung in a hardware shop* is a fable set to music in which, with many puns and plays on words, the poet makes his point, and like the hammer of the story, drives it home.

It is not long before Bunthorne discovers that Patience really loves Grosvenor. He upbraids her angrily, and the poor girl sings dolefully *Love is a plaintive song*. She goes off weeping, and Bunthorne pours out his rage and jealousy to Lady Jane. The faithful middle-aged lady is ever at hand, it seems, to cheer him up.

Bunthorne finally comes to the conclusion that Grosvenor's appeal lies in the fact that he is so mild and canonical. He decides to go to the mild poet and insist that he drop his aestheticism and become just an ordinary young man. In this way Bunthorne will have the poetic field to himself. Lady Jane agrees that this is the right thing to do, and joins Bunthorne in a duet which is jolly good fun:

> "Sing 'Booh to you—pooh, pooh to you'—
> Sing 'Bah to you—ha! ha! to you'—
> Sing 'Hey to you—good day to you'—
> And that's what $\begin{Bmatrix} I \\ you \end{Bmatrix}$ shall say!"
> And that's what $\begin{Bmatrix} I \\ you \end{Bmatrix}$ shall say!"

At this point in comes the trio of Dragoon officers, dressed in outrageous copies of the poetic garb of the aesthetes. They have long hair, and walk in stiff, constrained attitudes to music as angular and jerky as their poses. In an attempt to win back their sweethearts, they have decided that they will act like the poets. Angela and Saphir watch them. These two girls are touched by the Dragoons' show of devotion, and decide to return to their military lovers. But since there are three officers and only two girls in this scene, they have a tough problem to solve.

Some of Sullivan's merriest music accompanies the dance and song in which the Duke, the Colonel, and the Major try to decide who is to marry whom. The amusing lines

"In that case unprecedented,
Single I shall live and die—
I shall have to be contented
With their heartfelt sympathy!"

are sung by each of the men in turn, as the other two pair off with
Angela and Saphir. Finally, the Colonel and the Major get the
girls, and the Duke dances off by himself.

Bunthorne tackles Grosvenor and tells him that he must consent
to return to commonplace life and leave the aesthetic field to him.
To his surprise, Grosvenor, who has been wanting an excuse to
give up his posing, agrees. Their duet *When I go out of door* is
funny and gay, though not notable for its musical setting.

When Patience discovers that Grosvenor has undergone a complete change, she decides that now it will be all right for her to
marry him. He is no longer perfect. Bunthorne, from the aesthetic
point of view, has become so. To marry such perfection would be
a selfish act.

Bunthorne, crushed by Patience's decision, is about to console
himself by pairing off with Lady Jane when the Duke dances in
and persuades the aging charmer to take him instead. Bunthorne,
abandoned by all, sings:

"In that case unprecedented,
Single I must live and die—"

And the rest conclude the opera with:

"Each of us will wed the other,
Nobody be Bunthorne's bride!"

That was a typical Gilbertian conclusion for a piece subtitled
"Bunthorne's Bride."

For some time, Carte had been busy with plans for a new theater for the operas. He chose a site close to the Savoy Chapel, on the very spot where the Savoy Palace of John of Gaunt and the Duke of Lancaster had stood in the days of the Wars of the Roses. On October 10th, 1881, the famous Savoy Theatre was ready, and Carte transferred *Patience* from the Opéra Comique to ring up the first curtain. Here in this attractive theater decorated in tasteful Renaissance style all the rest of the Gilbert and Sullivan operas were performed, so that they became known as the Savoy Operas, and the "fans" who attended year in and year out, as "Savoyards."

In the years of Gilbert's and Sullivan's greatest popularity, the audiences which came to the Savoy knew all the previous operas so well that they put in the waiting time before the curtain went up singing the lovely, frolicsome songs of the earlier works. Because of the church-choir experience of the Victorians, many of them knew something about part-singing. The impromptu serenade from the audience was often a genuinely beautiful performance.

There is a story told of Oscar Wilde's lecture tour of America. Though England was well acquainted with this poet and his mediaeval cult, America knew very little about him. It occurred to Carte that the subject of a burlesque must be known if the point of the take-off is not to be lost. Though neither he nor Wilde ever admitted it, there seems to be considerable evidence that the clever partner of Gilbert and Sullivan arranged to send the poet, long hair, knee-breeches, lily and all to make himself known in all the principal cities of the United States. If it was a publicity stunt, it was a most daring and successful one. There are older residents of Denver, Colorado, for instance, who still snort indignantly when they recall Wilde's parading through the city streets with a *sun-*

flower in his lapel. The groundwork had been laid. America was ready to laugh as heartily as England at the aesthetes.

The Colonel's lusty song was one of the "hits" of the opera, both in London and in New York. It is a happy blending of Gilbert's humor with Sullivan's buoyant music:

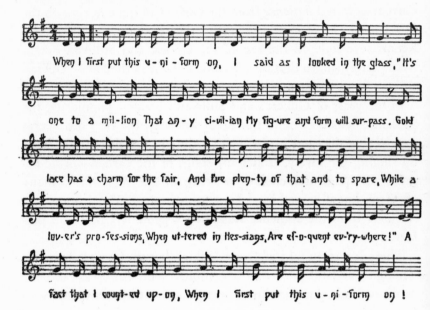

When I first put this u-ni-form on, I said as I looked in the glass, "It's one to a mil-lion That an-y ci-vil-ian My fig-ure and form will sur-pass. Gold lace has a charm for the fair, And I've plen-ty of that and to spare, While a lov-er's pro-fes-sions, When ut-tered in Hes-sians, Are el-o-quent ev-'ry-where!" A fact that I count-ed up-on, When I first put this u-ni-form on!

None shall part us from each oth - er,

7

GILBERT and Sullivan went to sea during the summer of 1881. Gilbert, the real sailorman, was in command of his own yacht, which went poking about the picturesque harbors and inlets of the south of England and Cornwall. Sullivan, darling of princes and noblemen, went as the guest of the Duke of Edinburgh on a cruise to the Baltic with the Reserve Squadron of the British Navy, of which the Duke was commander. Fred Clay went along as holiday guest on board *H.M.S. Hercules*.

The voyage was a gay holiday for Sullivan. When the *Hercules* was sailing, he lazed on deck, ate immoderately, and organized impromptu concerts with the ship's musicians. When the *Hercules* was in port, he dressed up and went along with the Duke and Clay to various dinners of state. At Copenhagen they were entertained by the royal family at a banquet to which one hundred persons sat down, and for which Danish musicians played Sullivan's music. In a letter to his mother, Sullivan described the confusion which came of the orchestra's repeating certain parts of the English national anthem. The guests had risen, of course, as the opening notes were played, but every time they thought the music was over and that it was time to sit down again, the orchestra would repeat the tune. Consequently, some of the diners were sitting and some rising all during the music, and everyone was flustered. Sullivan, the Duke, and Clay thought the incident was funny.

From Copenhagen, they sailed to Kronstadt, where the Russian ships greeted them with gun salutes and flag-dipping. The Czar's private yacht was waiting to take them to Peterhof, the summer palace. Sullivan's letters home contain a surprised allusion to the primitive sanitary arrangements in this palace of the most auto-cratic ruler in Europe, and to the odd circumstance of finding a Cossack guard sleeping on the mat outside his bedroom door. Alexander II had recently been assassinated, and his successor Alexander III, was taking no chances on his own life or the lives of palace guests. Sullivan's most memorable experience in Russia was hearing the famous Imperial Chapel Choir at the Winter Palace. There were about eighty singers, all in their striking formal dress of red and gold. Sullivan wrote home:

". . . *blasé* as I am with music, I confess to a new sensation at hearing them. It's like nothing else. They have basses with the most wonderful voices going down to the *low A,* and the effect of their singing was thrilling. Sometimes it was exactly like an organ only more beautiful. They sang for an hour, and I could have heard them for a couple of hours more."

This experience made such a deep impression on the composer that all his subsequent composing for voices *a capella* was colored by it. Many a beautiful quartet in the later operas owes its richness to the fine singing of the Russians.

On the way home, they stopped at Kiel, where they were met by Prince William (afterwards Kaiser William II) of Prussia. This

German ruler lost his throne when his armies were defeated on the battlefields of World War I. In Sullivan's day, however, he was a powerful prince. He showed only his pleasant side to his guests from across the Channel, and had the humor to greet the English composer by singing, "He polished up the handle of the big front door."

While Sullivan was making this round of the royal courts, Gilbert had been finishing the libretto for a successor to *Patience*. As much as he hated to get down to the drudgery of composing another long work, Sullivan returned to England in time to confer with Gilbert on the new story. He stayed in London long enough to move into his final home, Queen's Mansions in Victoria Street, and to conduct the first night at the Savoy.

News of the amazing innovations at the Savoy Theatre brought Londoners by the thousands. It was the first theater in London to be lighted entirely by electricity. Gas lighting also was installed "for emergencies." For the first time, too, free programs were provided, coat and hat checking was done without charge, and the queue system of buying seats was established. Londoners were further treated to a theater of beautiful decoration. The main color tones were white, pale yellow, and gold in tasteful Italian Renaissance design. Splashes of Venetian red in the boxes, brocaded curtains of yellow for the boxes, a creamy satin curtain for the stage, and inky blue plush for the stalls and the balcony seats made a striking color scheme.

With *Patience* moved over from the Opéra Comique and launched successfully at the Savoy Theatre, Sullivan packed his bags and went gayly off for another three-month vacation, this time to Egypt. His letters home were filled with his impressions of Oriental sights, sounds, and smells. Dancing dervishes, mosques,

bazaars, camel-trips to the pyramids, street musicians playing the
out—these things occupied his attention until he discovered that
his fortieth birthday was at hand. He rushed home to celebrate it
with his mother, who had been ailing for some time past, though
she had said very little about her illness. Two weeks later, Mother
Sullivan was dead. The last member of that wonderful family of
the composer's was gone. There were left to him only Fred's
children, whom he supported until their mother remarried and
moved with her husband to the United States.

After the funeral services for his mother, conducted by dear old
Thomas Helmore, the composer returned home desolate and
grief-stricken. In his diary, he wrote: "Home, feeling dreadfully
lonely." The very brevity of the comment makes it the more
poignant.

Shortly afterward, he went down to Cornwall to stay at the
home of Lady Molesworth, who had assured him that none of her
guests would disturb him during his composing hours. While he
was there, he would come down early to help himself to eggs and
bacon and steak-and-kidney pie from the sideboard, and then go
back to his room for the rest of the day. At dinner, he joined the
others and refused to talk of his work, preferring to forget his
serious labors in a game of cards. The music of *Iolanthe,* as the
new opera was eventually called, was taking shape.

The composer was not satisfied with Gilbert's first act, and
wrote to tell him so. Gilbert's yacht was poking about various
Cornish harbors; so it was arranged that he would put in at a
convenient port and meet Sullivan at the Half Moon Hotel in
Exeter. Over platters of ham and eggs, they began the recasting
of the act. They finished the revisions during dinner, and Gilbert
handed Sullivan Act Two as well. In this casual way, the partners
worked most effectively.

Sullivan suffered considerably from his nagging kidney complaint during the composition of *Iolanthe*. His illness was aggravated by the enormous amount of work he did in a short time. It had been decided to send a completely rehearsed cast to America to put on the opera simultaneously with the opening in London, in order to protect the performing rights in the United States. This meant that Sullivan had to complete his scoring much sooner than he usually did. He worked from sundown to sunup, rested a few hours, attended rehearsals, and came home to begin work again. The complete score was ready when the boat sailed for America, and a brilliant *premiere* was given in New York five hours after the London *premiere* at the Savoy.

Gilbert's libretto was suggested by his own *Bab Ballad, The Fairy Curate,* and ideas from a number of other "Babs" went into it, too. In a way that only he was capable of, Gilbert combined fairies, Dresden-china shepherd and shepherdess, and members of the House of Peers in a story of charm, biting wit, and sharp political satire. Sullivan wrote beautiful music for this opera. Carte gave it a magnificent staging, in which for the first time electric lights were used as costume details. The first-night audience cheered the production hysterically when the final curtain fell on the "fairy opera" the night of November 25th, 1882.

The solemn opening notes of Sullivan's Overture, and the fairy music of the reeds which follows, recalls delicate passages in his *Tempest* music. He draws on the pastoral themes of the opera throughout, so that his short prelude is quiet and delicate, a tone poem in reflective mood.

At the rising of the curtain, a chorus of fairies sing and dance in a ring in a meadow, through which flows a small stream spanned by a rustic bridge. Gilbert's fairies are human through and through, it must be confessed, but Sullivan's music for their *Tripping hither, tripping thither* is really out of fairyland.

The fairies are not really very gay, despite their dancing. Their beloved sister, Iolanthe, has been banished by the Fairy Queen for the fairy crime of marrying a mortal, and since during her exile she has elected to live at the bottom of the stream among the frogs, her sisters have been doubly sad. Fairy revels have not been the same, they tell their Queen, begging her to forgive Iolanthe and allow her to return.

The Queen consents, saying that she had no idea that Iolanthe would add to her punishment by going to live in her wet prison. The composer provided an exquisite musical setting for the invocation to Iolanthe to rise from the stream.

Beautiful Iolanthe comes in answer to the call, and tells why it is that she chose the stream during her exile from the meadow. It seems that she and her mortal husband had a son, Strephon, a shepherd who watches his flocks on the bank of the stream. Iolanthe chose to live in her uncomfortable watery prison to be near him.

Strephon enters singing, dancing, and playing on a flageolet. Sullivan's music for Gilbert's graceful song is tender and tuneful.

> "Good morrow, good mother!
> Good mother, good morrow!"

is in just the right spirit for a shepherd-lad who has obviously just stepped out of a Watteau tapestry.

The fairies greet him with both surprise and pleasure. He is assured that if ever he needs their help, they will come flying to his aid. It would seem that he might need this help, too, for he is in love with Phyllis, a ward-in-chancery, and the Lord Chancellor refuses to give his permission for the marriage. Matters are complicated by the fact, which Strephon keeps a strict secret, that he is only half human. He is a fairy down to his waist, but his legs are mortal. And, as he says, what is the good of your upper part being able to slip through a key hole if your legs stick?

Phyllis comes dancing into the meadow, singing "Good morrow, good lover!" to the tune of Strephon's song. She is a dainty little Dresden-china shepherdess, and anyone can understand why Strephon feels that the sooner they are married, the better. It seems that half the House of Lords is seeking her hand in marriage. Phyllis reassures Strephon of her love with *None shall part us from each other*. There is no lovelier song in the Gilbert and Sullivan collection than this one. In the duet, the voices answer each other tenderly, and then combine in poignant harmony.

Phyllis and Strephon are no sooner out of the way than the Peers enter in procession. To Gilbert's bitterly satiric verses, Sullivan contributed a perfect setting. Opening with a noble fanfare of horns, the music marches majestically through the orchestral score into the chorus of men's voices. Here are pomp and circumstance, all the pageantry and color of aristocratic power unchallenged. Sullivan, always a master of choral writing, gave to *Loudly let the trumpet bray!* a special richness of harmony which recalls the fact that he learned something from the singing of the wonderful Russian choir of St. Petersburg. Gilbert's words, too, despite their purely humorous meaning, achieved a striking sonority admirably suited to such a setting.

Following this lordly procession of the Peers in gorgeous robes and coronets, the Lord Chancellor, a dapper little man in a large wig, sings the comic

"The Law is the true embodiment
Of everything that's excellent."

He complains in extremely funny verse that it is very trying for
him to have to be the guardian of pretty young girls and give them
in marriage to others, when he himself would like to marry one:

> "With one for him—and one for he—
> And one for you—and one for ye—
> And one for thou—and one for thee—
> But never, oh, never a one for me!
>   Which is exasperating for
>   A highly susceptible Chancellor!"

He discusses the situation with Lords Tolloller and Mountararat.
All of them love Phyllis, who at that moment comes to meet them
in obedience to her guardian's summons. Lord Tolloller sings her
his proposal of marriage, ending with

> "Her origin's lowly, it's true,
>   I've grammar and spelling for two."

Lord Mountararat also proposes, but Phyllis declines both offers
of marriage, declaring that
> "In lowly cot
>   Alone is virtue found!"

But the chorus of Peers, shocked, cries:
> "No, no indeed high rank will never hurt you,
>   The Peerage is not destitute of virtue."

Whereupon Tolloller the eloquent defends the "nobly born," declaring that

> "High rank involves no shame—
> We boast an equal claim
> With him of humble name
>   To be respected!"

It is amusing to compare Gilbert's words to those of his friend Robertson, who had said in all seriousness in *Caste:*

> "Kind hearts are more than coronets,
>   And simple faith than Norman blood!"

Gilbert was surely remembering that aside when he wrote the words of Lord Tolloller's mock-serious song.

Phyllis, distressed, tells them that her heart is already given, and Strephon rushes in to claim his love and defy the Lord Chancellor himself. Though this is a staggering blow, the lords are able to depart "dignified and stately" to the music of Sullivan's glorious *March of the Peers.*

The Chancellor angrily sends Phyllis away, and begins to upbraid Strephon, who, for a dainty shepherd boy, holds his ground remarkably well. He says that all nature approves the match, and asks the Chancellor how he can have the heart to refuse his consent. The Chancellor says that it is his duty to refuse. He declares that he owes his success to this sense of duty. His song *When I went to the Bar as a very young man* is one of those humorous autobiographical ditties for which the Judge in *Trial by Jury* set the pattern.

When the Chancellor is gone, Strephon calls to his mother. She comforts him by telling him that the fairies will come to his aid. Strephon thanks her in a tender little scene, witnessed by the Lords and Phyllis, who have come in on tiptoe. The quartet of the *Finale* is built around a series of misunderstandings. Phyllis and the others hear only fragments of what Iolanthe and Strephon say to each other; their imaginations supply the rest.

Phyllis is in anguish, thinking that Strephon is untrue to her, since Iolanthe, being an ageless fairy, looks like a young girl. When she accuses Strephon of double dealing, he tells her frankly that

Iolanthe is his mother. The Lords turn from him in derisive laughter, singing "But to find a mother younger than her son is very curious." Phyllis in pique announces that she is ready to marry either Tolloller or Mountararat and she doesn't care which!

The Fairy Queen arrives to bear out the story of Iolanthe and Strephon, but the Peers, mistaking her for the proprietor of a Ladies' Seminary, tell her to "Beware, madam, and begone!"

Angered, the Queen tells them that she is "an influential fairy," that she intends to have Strephon enter Parliament, where he will give them plenty of trouble. Her song which begins

> "Henceforth, Strephon, cast away
> Crooks and pipes and ribbons so gay—"

has a jocund tune written for voices unaccompanied. There is nothing more light-hearted than the way the chorus and soloists play with the words "Into Parliament he shall go!"

The act ends with the hilarious Ensemble built on the tune for *Young Strephon is the kind of lout we do not care a fig about!*

Act Two takes place in the palace yard of Westminster. Private Willis standing sentry duty by moonlight sings about how comical it is that Nature always does contrive

> "That every boy and every gal
>   That's born into the world alive,
>   Is either a little Liberal
>   Or else a little Conservative."

The fairies and the Peers meet under the big clock of Westminster Hall. The Peers complain of how their lives are being made miserable by Strephon, who carries every measure he proposes. Then Lord Mountarrarat sings a solemn song in Sullivan's

best national anthem style, *When Britain really ruled the waves.*
Gilbert's wit cut deep in such lines as

> "When Wellington thrashed Bonaparte,
>   As every child can tell,
> The House of Peers, throughout the war,
> Did nothing in particular,
>   And did it very well."

Meanwhile, the fairies have been looking the Peers over, and
find them very attractive. The Fairy Queen enters, takes in the
situation at a glance, and warns them that to marry a mortal is a
serious offense. She confesses that she finds Private Willis almost
irresistible, but that it is necessary to put this weakness away. The
rest agree, though one of the fairies says ruefully, "We know it's
weakness, but the weakness is so strong!"

When the Fairy Queen sang that, though her heart was as soft
as her sister fairies', she was determined to quench the flame of
love with the water of common sense, she asked:

> "Oh, Captain Shaw!
>   Type of true love kept under!
>   Could thy brigade
>   With cold cascade
>   Quench my great love, I wonder!"

The first-night audience at the Savoy howled with mirth. Captain
E. M. Shaw, Chief of the London Fire Brigade, was in the
audience, the picture of utter amazement to discover himself the
butt of a practical joke.

When the sorrowful Queen and her fairies leave, Phyllis enters
and meets her two aristocratic suitors face to face. There is some

amusing dialogue, in which the girl begs the men not to fight over
her. Tolloller and Mountararat decide that she is right, friendship should take precedence over love. Private Willis joins in the
quartet of friendship, after which the four go off in the friendliest
possible spirit.

The Lord Chancellor enters, very miserable, sighing that *Love,
unrequited love, robs me of my rest*. This is a difficult and clever
patter song on the subject of insomnia and dreams. Sullivan's
music takes a background position until the very last words, when
with a subtle change of key, he abandons the eerie quality of the
nightmare and returns to a sane world with the words:

> "But the darkness has passed, and it's daylight at last, and
> the night has been long—ditto my song—and thank
> goodness they're both of them over!"

Lords Tolloller and Mountararat find the Chancellor in very
low spirits indeed. When they learn the reason, they encourage
him to woo his ward Phyllis. Since they have decided to give up
love for friendship, they can be generous about the matter. The
Lord Chancellor takes heart and joins them in the amusing trio
Faint heart never won fair lady! They dance out arm-in-arm.

Strephon and Phyllis meet, and confess that they have been
miserable about the misunderstanding. They decide to forget their
differences and get married. Their duet *If we're weak enough to
tarry* is a dainty tune with a folk-song quality.

Iolanthe joins them and tells them her secret. The Lord Chancellor is her husband, and Strephon's father. Strephon and Phyllis
hurry off when they see the Chancellor approaching, but Iolanthe,
wearing a veil to conceal her features, stays to plead for her son.
She begs that he give his consent to the marriage of his ward with

Strephon. The composer gave her song such sincere music that her plea is strangely moving. The Chancellor is touched, but remains firm in his refusal. He tells Iolanthe that he intends to marry Phyllis himself.

"No, no!" cries Iolanthe. She sees that she must reveal to him that she is his wife, even though this will break the fairy law. Once more she breaks her vows, and her sister fairies cry in the distance, "Forbear!" The music for the wailing of the fairies is both mournful and weird. The strange words, "Aiaiah! Aiaiah!" are surely the wailing of the Irish banshees.

The Chancellor is overcome when Iolanthe throws off her veil and he sees before him the wife he had thought dead. The Queen of the Fairies pronounces Iolanthe's doom, and is about to hurl her spear, when the rest of the fairies cry out that she must kill them all, for they are all married to members of the House of Peers. The Queen is dumbfounded. What to do! She finds it difficult to bring herself to destroy all the fairies.

At that point, the Lord Chancellor, good lawyer that he is, finds a way out. The fairy law reads, "Every fairy marrying a mortal must die!" Well, just insert the word *not* before *marrying*—and there you are! The Queen finds this a good solution, and promptly selects Private Willis for her husband. With the consent of the Peers, she touches them with her wand. All sprout wings and fly away with their fairy wives to fairyland to the flippant little song *Up in the air, sky-high, sky-high.*

Nothing in the music of *Iolanthe* reflected the composer's grief for his mother, which had been his constant companion during the writing of the whole opera. And nothing in the composer's manner betrayed the fact that a few moments before he raised his baton to begin the Overture for the delightful fairy opera, news had come to him that a firm entrusted with his savings had gone bankrupt. Sullivan was a real trouper.

The success of *Iolanthe* was immediate and complete. Two days after the first-night performance, all seats at the Savoy were sold out for the coming year. When the music of the songs with piano accompaniment was published by the house of Chappell, ten thousand copies were mailed in a single day. Prime Minister Gladstone came to see the opera, and took the trouble to write from No. 10 Downing Street to say, "I must thankfully acknowledge the great pleasure which the entertainment gave me."

The partnership had never seemed so secure. Gilbert and Sullivan had become an institution. No one could imagine them working apart. And then the lozenge popped up.

But meanwhile, all London went about singing the charming songs from *Iolanthe*. A good many hesitating lovers made up their minds to take the plunge as they hummed the tune of *If we're weak enough to tarry:*

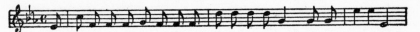

Yet ev-'ry-bo-dy says I'm such a dis-a-gree-able man! And I can't think why!

8

HE new year 1883 found Sullivan in Paris, enjoying his old haunts and refusing even to think about music. Gilbert, on the contrary, was bothering his head about a new opera. It would have been wiser if he had followed his partner's example. As it was, he was in a bad temper most of the time. The more the new plot eluded him, the more testy he became. Never had adverse criticism affected him so much. His wife formed the habit of cutting out reviews from the newspapers and periodicals, and showing her husband only the favorable ones.

Some time before, at a dinner party, Gilbert had crossed swords with the editor of *Punch*. The playwright had asked sarcastically, "Do you never get good jokes for your magazine, Burnand?"

"Oh, frequently!" Burnand turned the thrust aside with a laugh.

"Then why don't you publish them?" Gilbert drove his rapier home, and enjoyed the general laugh at Burnand's expense.

But Gilbert did not enjoy the article which Burnand printed in criticism of *Iolanthe*. The editor had his revenge before a larger audience than a dinner party. He charged that Gilbert's songs were not original, insisting that the Lord Chancellor's song was

139

cribbed from an old ditty, *Says I to myself as I walked by myself.*

Burnand's criticism was ill-natured and unjust. Gilbert may have been influenced by his reading, a situation proper and inevitable for an artist; but he was never guilty of direct theft of another's ideas.

Artistic competition and jealousy was the real root of the feud. Just as Gilbert never forgave Burnand for calling his favorite play *Broken Hearts* "Broken Parts," Burnand, who wrote the libretto of *Cox and Box,* could not forgive Gilbert for taking Composer Sullivan away from him.

Gilbert was having his troubles at the Savoy, too, where as Director he watched over the performers as well as the performances. Someone jokingly referred to the Savoy as the Young Ladies' Seminary after several amusing incidents in which Gilbert proved to the world at large that *his* company was composed of ladies and gentlemen. One of these episodes involved the youthful singer Jessie Bond. Between the acts of *Iolanthe,* a group of young blades in one of the boxes sent her a note in which they invited her to dinner with them. Gilbert demanded to see the note, and forthwith charged like a lion on the offenders, ordering them to leave the theater at once or be thrown out, whichever they preferred. He meant what he said, too. The astonished young men filed meekly out, probably never saw the second act of *Iolanthe,* and very likely cherished a life-long grudge against the Gilbert and Sullivan operas.

Gilbert was a man who bent destiny to his will. When he discovered that the ordinary tennis court was too small for his smashing drive, he had the court at his home lengthened. Another man might have shortened his stroke, but not Gilbert! Finding the theater of his day coarse, he determined to reform it. Refinement of speech and conduct was required of his artists. Respect for them was required of his audiences.

Gilbert finally decided that an opera based on his play *The Wicked World* would be a good idea. Because there were fairies in this work, Carte vetoed the idea. Gilbert had to lay this project aside, though he stubbornly refused to abandon it. Twelve years later he got Edward German to write the music for the libretto, and the work was produced as *Fallen Fairies*. It was staged at the Savoy, too. Gilbert, like a dog with a bone, could hang on tenaciously.

Gilbert went back to his study and thought again. This time he outlined a story about a magic lozenge. Whoever ate it, immediately became whatever or whomever he pretended to be. Though it was not a bad plot, when Sullivan read it he was as much against the lozenge as Carte had been against following the fairies of *Iolanthe* with more fairies.

Why? Gilbert wanted to know. He could not understand what was wrong. Sullivan, pressed for an explanation, made a slighting remark about the magic lozenge. He did not want to work with another story of unreality. He definitely did not care to set music to "clock-work and springs"—or lozenges. He wanted a romantic story, with humor growing naturally out of real-life, not fairyland, situations. Gilbert shook his head, put his story on the shelf, and growled at everyone who came near him while he searched his poor tired brain for a new idea.

The best he could do was to go back to an early play *The Princess,* in which he had burlesqued Tennyson's poem. He called his libretto *Princess Ida; or, Castle Adamant.* Sullivan was not very enthusiastic about it, but he and Gilbert had just signed a five-year agreement with Carte and something had to be written

He and Gilbert discussed the first act in February, and they were still discussing the story in July. Finally, the book shaped up to the composer's satisfaction. He gave his nod of approval during a visit to the Gilberts at Eastbury, one of the few occasions when the collaborators met on a social basis. As a rule, they met to discuss business only, usually at the theater.

Gilbert, working away at the last minor changes suggested by Sullivan, found his patience wearing thin. His mood was not improved when he learned that Sullivan had been invited, along with Grove and Macfarren, to go to Windsor Castle to receive the sword tap which would make him a knight. Gilbert and Sullivan were a team. The Queen was slapping the playwright's wrist by honoring only the musical partner. It was a bitter pill to swallow, bitterer even than the lozenge which the composer refused to swallow.

He covered up his resentment, of course, and even condescended to attend Sullivan's forty-first birthday dinner at the composer's home in Queen's Mansions. The names of the dinner guests read like a Social Register—the Prince of Wales, the Duke of Edinburgh, the Marquis of Hartington, the Earl of Kenmare, Ferdinand Rothschild, Sir John Everett Millais. Gilbert felt like a bull in a china shop.

Madame Albani and Composer Tosti furnished the musical entertainment. As a surprise, Sullivan had rigged up a telephone between his rooms and the Savoy Theatre. The whole Savoy company had been instructed to assemble and sing selections from *Iolanthe*. It was such a novel stunt in those days to hear a play by telephone that it became the talk of London. Radio was unheard-of, and would have seemed a fantastic and impossible dream to Sullivan's guests.

Gilbert snorted his disapproval. Much more sensible to go to the theater and hear the opera properly, he thought. He was out of sympathy with the whole fashionable affair. Even the wonderful dinner cooked by Sullivan's French chef failed to appease him. He once remarked: "My cook gets eighty pounds a year and gives me a kipper. Sullivan's cook gets five hundred pounds a year for giving him the same thing in French."

Nearly the whole of the fall of 1883 was spent on the music of *Princess Ida*. Gilbert had departed from the old pattern. The new work was in three acts and in blank verse. Setting it gave Sullivan trouble. Much of the comedy of the libretto was forced, many of the verses insipid. Sullivan enjoyed setting King Gama's songs, however, possibly because this character possessed a number of Gilbert's own unpleasant traits and it was a joy to the composer to add to the caricature.

It was soon apparent that the collaborators were out of sympathy with each other. When Gilbert read the book to the assembled company at the Savoy, Sullivan found some excuse to be absent. During the rehearsals, the players were affected by the general ill-humor. Serious friction developed.

Gilbert was a regular bear. The actors could do nothing to please him. They had trouble with the blank verse, probably because Gilbert was more exacting than usual, and had less patience, if that were possible. One player, trying his best to speak his lines, could hardly get two words together out of his mouth before the playwright interrupted. Exasperated, he snapped, "Look here, Mr. Gilbert, I know my lines!"

"But you don't know mine," was the sharp rebuke.

When the play seemed to be going better, Gilbert would disappear for a time. Just as the poor players thought that he was satisfied at last, he would pop up from one of the front seats of the theater shouting balefully, "What on *earth* do you think you're doing?"

Even the sunny-tempered Sullivan, who it has been said could get more out of an orchestra and chorus than any other conductor of his time, not by bullying but by *leading,* sometimes lost his temper during the *Princess Ida* rehearsals. One of the actor-singers persisted in interpreting a song as Sullivan did not want it. The composer patiently told him over and over how the song should be sung. The man obstinately sang it his way. Finally Sullivan exploded. "Either you do not understand that song, or I don't," he said.

"I think *I* understand it," retorted the singer.

"Perhaps you do, That's the worst of being a composer. One always begins at the wrong end of the stick. In future, I shall get you to sing my songs first, and I'll compose them afterward."

There was a shocked silence. Not only the offending singer but also the rest of the cast was amazed. This sort of thing was expected from Gilbert, but Sullivan's way was to invite a singer home and coach him in private, so that he would not be held up to ridicule before the others. Something was wrong with the partnership.

Something was wrong with Sullivan, too. A good many things, in fact. His painful kidney trouble was at times almost unbearable. His good friend, Fred Clay, had a paralytic stroke just a week before the new opera opened. Sullivan, seeing poor Fred, who had always been so gay and care-free, lying in a state of coma, could not work, even though he was already late with the score. At Christmas, his sister-in-law married B. C. Hutchinson and moved to California. Herbert Sullivan stayed with his uncle, but even so, Sullivan felt that his last link with the past had been severed, and a terrible loneliness came over him.

Princess Ida was scheduled for production four days after New Year's. The composer drove himself mercilessly to meet the deadline. The result was that his body did not stand the strain. He completed the music by working all through the night of New Year's Eve. He rehearsed the orchestra next day, and composed some last-minute songs in the days that followed. He attended a full-dress rehearsal the day before the opening. Everything went wrong, and the poor players were kept at the theater until 2:30 in the morning. Then he collapsed.

Sullivan's doctor forbade him to conduct the opening-night performance, but Sullivan's will overruled this advice. With a strong injection of morphine to ease his pain, and a cup of strong coffee to keep him awake, he managed to get to the theater. The warm reception of the audience buoyed him up. The performance went without a hitch, but after the final curtain, the composer fainted, and had to be brought home by his nephew and Frank Cellier.

Princess Ida was given a magnificent mounting by Carte. Colorful and rich mediaeval costumes, romantic castle sets, and authentic armor for the battle scenes brought exclamations of surprise and pleasure from the audience on the night of January 5th, 1884.

The curtain rises to discover King Hildebrand, his soldiers and courtiers in an elaborate pavilion attached to Hildebrand's palace. Everyone is staring intently at the road along which they expect to see King Gama approaching, for this is the day agreed on for him to bring his daughter, Ida, to wed Hilarion, son of King Hildebrand. There is considerable doubt whether King Gama

will keep his bargain. To be on the safe side, King Hildebrand
has ordered two kinds of receptions for the royal guests.

"For Gama place the richest robes we own—
For Gama place the coarsest prison dress—"

The lines are mildly amusing, and Sullivan's music is adequate,
but little more can be said for the opening solos and chorus.

Hilarion's ballad explains how he and Ida were married when
"Ida was a twelvemonth old" and he was "twice her age, twenty
years ago!"

It seems that for some time Ida has dedicated herself to the
advancement of women's rights, and has even become the head
of a women's university. King Hildebrand thinks that a wife
dedicated to "stern philosophies" is no bargain, but Hilarion, remembering his blushing baby bride "all bib and tucker, frill and
furbelow" is loth to give her up.

The sons of King Gama—Arac, Guron, and Scynthius—enter in
full armor. They are great lumbering louts, for whom Sullivan
wrote some good and appropriate music. They are satirical take-
offs on the professional soldier. Perhaps Gilbert had in mind
Tennyson's absurd philosophy of "Their's not to reason why,
their's but to do or die" when he penned the lines:

"Bold, and fierce, and strong, ha! ha!
     For a war we burn,
  With its right or wrong, ha! ha!
  We have no concern."

King Gama enters, with one of the two best songs of the opera
(the other being his, too). People who knew Gilbert were sure
that in a moment of reckless honesty and self-analysis, he had

described himself in this song. The last stanza gives a good idea
of the whole:

"I'm sure I'm no ascetic; I'm as pleasant as can be;
　You'll always find me ready with a crushing repartee,
　I've an irritating chuckle, I've a celebrated sneer,
　I've an entertaining snigger, I've a fascinating leer.
　To everybody's prejudice I know a thing or two;
　I can tell a woman's age in half a minute—and I do.
　But although I try to make myself as pleasant as I can,
　Yet everybody says I am a disagreeable man.
　　And I can't think why!"

King Gama is a well-drawn character throughout, in dialogue
as well as song. He is spiteful, bitter, sly, and generally unpleasant
—yet he seems to have a wholesome regard for his strong-minded
daughter, and any sneers in the opera at women's intelligence and
capacity for learning do not come from him. Like Gilbert himself,
he is contradictory.

He tells King Hildebrand that there is no hope of getting Ida
to carry out the marriage bargain. She and her students have shut
themselves away from the world of men, whom they scorn.
Nothing masculine is permitted within the walls of Castle
Adamant, not so much as a rooster or set of chessmen.

Today, Gilbert's idea of an "advanced" woman seems odd, to
say the least. In the modern world, where the right of women
to culture and knowledge is taken for granted in all nations which
pretend to progress, the point of the satire is lost. Princess Ida and
her students are nothing more or less than freaks, confusing "man-
hating" with equality for women.

It must be remembered, however, that in Victorian England women were either poor hopeless drudges, working from morning to night, at scrubbing floors or pulling trams in the coal-mine tunnels; or they were useless, aimless, dependent creatures living on the bounty of husband, brother, or other male relative. Gilbert probably did not number among his personal friends many scrub women or mine workers; it never occurred to him that such women, of the "lower classes" as he would have said, were even capable of anything better than gin-guzzling. As for the kind of women he knew—women like his wife, his adopted daughter, actresses in his shows—what did they need an Oxford or Cambridge education for? To his way of thinking, a woman either married and was provided for by her husband; or she made the most of her beauty and went on the stage. A woman engineer? Physician? Chemist? Biologist? Prime Minister? Unthinkable! As for voting in the elections, well! Women were supposed to think about preparing meals, keeping the house clean, minding the baby, and saying *yes* to their husband's ideas.

Of course, in this, as in nearly everything else in life, Gilbert was not consistent. He liked women with brains. Nothing irritated him more than a silly, over-feminine creature who gushed and tittered and said, "Oh, Mr. Gilbert, how wonderful you are!" To one such woman, who made a big fuss over a bee which had landed on Gilbert's hand, he said, "Nothing to get excited about. I don't think he's fool enough to mistake me for a flower!"

Women were always in the majority at the dinners in the Gilbert home, the kind of women who knew how to make witty and intelligent conversation. Gilbert once remarked, "It isn't half so important what's on the table. It's what's on the chairs that counts." And it is certain that Gilbert, who liked to exchange ideas on nearly everything under the sun, did not care to have dull-witted guests on his dinner chairs.

As for women in business, the idea in the abstract seemed ridiculous to him. In reality, he did business for years with Miss Lenoir, secretary to and later wife of Richard D'Oyly Carte. A remarkable woman who was as able a manager as her husband, she often took complete charge at the theater when her husband was away on business for the company. Some of the hardest work on behalf of the Gilbert and Sullivan ventures was done by her, and many a brilliant promotion idea came from her brain. Gilbert was very fond of her, and respected her ability and integrity. The year of *Princess Ida* she made a business proposal to the playwright, suggesting that an agreement be signed. He wrote:

> "My dear Miss Lenoir,—
> I have the honour to be,
> Madame,
> Your very obliged and
> truly humble servant,
> W. S. Gilbert,
> and will therefore sign any blessed thing you tell me to."

This hardly seems the same man who in *Princess Ida* painted the grotesque picture of women aspiring to be free and independent. But to get back to King Gama and the others.

Both librettist and composer were up to their old form when they created the duet of Gama and Hildebrand, in which Gama suggests that Ida may *possibly* be won over if the matter is handled "Most politely, most politely," and Hildebrand assures Gama that if Ida does not give in, Hilarion will take her castle by storm. Gama is to be held hostage, so that should Hilarion disappear

"We will hang you, never fear,
    Most politely, most politely!"

Sullivan wrote some captivating music, too, for the *Trio,* sung
by Hilarion and his two friends, Cyril and Florian. They tell how
they will wage war on the girls of Castle Adamant:

"We'll storm their bowers
With scented showers
Of fairest flowers
    That we can buy."

The dainty chorus has a melody as frivolous and blithe as the
the words:

"Oh, dainty triolet!
Oh, fragrant violet!
Oh, gentle heigh-ho-let
    (Or little sigh).

Gama and his sons are thrust into a dungeon cell, and the act
closes with King Gama's lumbering, loutish boys singing their
protest and adding something about "the guns that go boom,
boom!"

Act Two opens on a beautiful pastoral scene. In the garden of
Castle Adamant, Lady Psyche is instructing a number of young
girls seated at her feet. Melissa asks her instructor for a list of
classical authors, but Sacharissa wants to know:

"Pray you, tell us, if you can
What's the thing that's known as Man?"

Psyche explains in an amusing song just what an inadequate
creature man is, and the chorus of students declare:

"We'll a memorandum make—
Man is Nature's sole mistake!"

A good deal of such "satire" follows, and then Princess Ida appears, to make her address to the new students. In spite of himself, Gilbert gave her a certain dignity and sincerity. Her plea to Minerva, *Oh, goddess wise* has real beauty.

Lady Blanche, another lecturer in this women's college, talks like a page of pie type. And she, of all people, is jealous of Ida, believing that she should be head of the college in place of the Princess. Her song *Come, mighty Must!* was too much for Sullivan. It inspired nothing new; so he went back to some discarded music from *Thespis* and adapted a ready-made tune for it.

Hilarion, Cyril, and Florian, disguised as girls, climb over the castle wall. Their *Trio* and dance is very good. Hilarion, with appropriate pantomime, shows how he intends to act the part of a "maiden cold and stately." Cyril will be a "maiden frank and simple," and Florian, a "maiden coyly blushing."

When the Princess comes in, they apply for admission to the college. The Princess is surely a true professor. She is all too glad to have three new recruits, and never thinks to ask how they got into the grounds. She welcomes them and goes on her way.

When Lady Psyche sees the three, matters are not so simple: for she is Florian's sister and recognizes him instantly. She proves to be a good sport, however, and though her song *The Lady and the Ape* seems to have very little to do with the case, one gathers that she does not intend to betray them. Melissa, who is Lady Blanche's daughter, comes upon the scene, and is frankly delighted. Sullivan wrote some roguish music for Gilbert's *Quintette,* which begins:

"The woman of the wisest wit
    May sometimes be mistaken, O!"

When Lady Blanche discovers the secret of the new "girls," she
is persuaded to say nothing, since, as Melissa slyly points out to her
mother, if she aids Hilarion's plan, it may well turn out that the
Princess will marry and go away. Then Lady Blanche can be head
of the college.

She and Melissa seal their bargain with the cheerful *Sing, hoity,
toity! Sorry for some!*

At luncheon, Cyril becomes very talkative. It is not long before
he is making statements which rouse the suspicions of the Princess.
Finally he sings the sprightly

"Would you know the kind of maid
    Sets my heart aflame-a?"

With this song, Gilbert proved that he could write in true romantic
vein, and Sullivan's music for the refrain

"Oh, kiss me, kiss me, kiss me, kiss me,
    Though I die of shame-a!"

has an ardor which the composer rarely permitted himself. The
two very proper Victorian gentlemen "let down their hair" for a
moment in a song which sounds more like Victor Herbert, the
Irish-American who knew a thing or two about writing lovers'
songs for operetta.

The Princess is aghast. She runs to the bridge, turns to fling
scorn in the faces of the imposters, and loses her balance. As she
struggles in the water, Hilarion jumps in and saves her. She loses
none of her indignation, however, and when she is on dry land

once more, she orders the arrest of the men. While his companions are being bound, Hilarion sings her a love song in which Gilbert caught the delicate beauty and courtliness of Herrick's poetry. Sullivan's setting for *Whom thou hast chained must wear his chain* is wistful and yearning.

There is a sudden change of mood with the announcement that Hildebrand and his soldiers are about to storm the castle. In fact, Hildebrand has already forced his way inside the walls. His solo, with the spirited

> "And I'm a peppery kind of King,
> Who's indisposed for parleying
> To fit the wit of a bit of a chit,
> And that's the long and the short of it!"

is a welcome return to more robust verses and tunes, after the long-sustained lyric mood of the passages preceding.

Princess Ida refuses to yield. She prepares to defend her castle.

Act Three opens just before the battle begins. The Princess addresses her girls, all of whom are armed with battle-axes. As she tells them what their duties are to be—one to take care of the wounded, one to bring up the gunpowder, others to form a rifle brigade, and so forth—they get weak-kneed and most of them desert her. This is not an attractive picture which Gilbert paints. Even the Victorian audiences seemed to resent the slur cast on the courage of women. Perhaps some of them were remembering the valiant Florence Nightingale.

In the face of the Englishwoman's record for calm bravery won during the robot-bombing of England during World War II, this part of *Princess Ida* would deserve to be hissed. Gilbert and Sullivan could not understand why this opera was a near failure.

They need have looked no further than the whimpering refrain of "Please you, do not hurt us," for their answer. They built on an idea which was unprogressive and false. Edvard Grieg could have told them what their trouble was. He once said, "If an artist is on the side of reaction, he is done for!"

Only for the Princess herself did Gilbert find sympathy in his heart. For her he wrote the pathetic *I built upon a rock,* and Sullivan gave it nobility with his stately music.

The Princess is informed that her father and brothers seek an audience. They have been sent to plead with Ida to surrender. Gama tells her that he is being tortured, but when he tells what his "torments" are, we see that Gilbert is having his joke again. Gama, the grumbler, has been given nothing to grumble at! He mourns:

> "O, don't the days seem lank and long
> When all goes right and nothing goes wrong,
> And isn't your life extremely flat
> With nothing whatever to grumble at!"

In this very funny song, the team of Gilbert and Sullivan were working together with all their old verve.

The Princess remains defiant, musters her forces, and a furious battle is waged. The girls lose, and the Princess agrees to go with her husband, Hilarion. Lady Psyche announces her intention of marrying Cyril, and Melissa joins her fortunes with those of Florian. Lady Blanche is left in charge of the college. Everybody is happy. Even the Princess confesses that she loves her husband and goes with him willingly. The *finale, With joy abiding,* is set to the winsome music of the *Trio* of Act One.

Opening night for *Princess Ida* in January—and by the end of

March the box office was already falling off sharply! Sullivan, ill and overworked as he had been just before the *premiere,* found the comparative failure hard to accept. He had counted on a long vacation, but instead he was informed by Carte that in accordance with the terms of their new agreement librettist and composer were being given six months' notice to have an opera ready for fall.

Sullivan could not, of course, refuse to do another opera, but he could give expression to his reluctance by finding fault with Gilbert's work. He wrote Carte that he could not set another book of the sort that his collaborator had been furnishing him. He made it quite clear that unless Gilbert would give up his charms, lozenges, and other supernatural elements, he would flatly refuse to go on. There were no lozenges in *Princess Ida* to account for his attititude. Carte was as amazed as Gilbert.

Gilbert wrote to ask Sullivan his true reasons and received a reply which must have astounded him. For the first time in the history of the partnership, Sullivan gave expression to a feeling of jealousy. He wrote from Paris:

"My tunes are in danger of becoming mere repetitions of my former pieces, my concerted movements are getting to possess a strong family likeness.

"I have rung all the changes possible in the way of variety of rhythm. It has hitherto been word setting, I might almost say syllable setting, for I have looked upon the words as being of such importance that I have been continually keeping down the music in order that not one should be lost.

"And this my suppression is most difficult, most fatiguing, and I may say most disheartening, for the music is never allowed to arise and speak for itself."

He went on to say that he did not want a break in their partnership, but that he must have a story of probability and human interest to set, "where the humorous words would come in a humorous (not serious) situation, and where, if the situation were a tender or dramatic one, the words would be of a similar character."

It was this last statement that stung Gilbert. He wrote a fiery letter in which he accused the composer of trying to teach him the ABC of his profession. "It is inconceivable," he said, "that any sane author should ever write other than as you propose I should write in future."

Back in London, Sullivan proposed that Gilbert meet him and talk the matter over. And Gilbert came, but the lozenge came also. Sullivan wrote in his diary: "Long argument on his part—no concession on either side—complete deadlock, though quite friendly throughout."

Gilbert suggested that Sullivan set a libretto by some other author. This was a generous gesture, and his partner appreciated the fact. Bret Harte was in England, making a lecture tour arranged by Carte's booking office. Someone suggested that he prepare a book for the composer, and he promptly adapted his *The Luck of Roaring Camp*. But Sullivan returned it to the American author with a note expressing his regrets. Years before, Sullivan had said of Gilbert, "After all, there's no one like him." His opinion still held.

While he was in this conciliatory mood, Gilbert decided that his stubborn sponsorship of the lozenge plot was not good business sense. He wrote Sullivan to say that he would abandon it and write a story along the lines suggested by the composer. Sullivan, relieved that the affair had taken a turn for the better, made a

friendly gesture of his own. He wrote back to say that he would
be glad to set such a piece "without further discussing the matter,
or asking what the subject is to be."

It was high time to begin another opera. *Princess Ida* was weak-
ening badly. The women were having the last word, and that
word was a disapproving one for the opera's views on the economic
and political rights of women. A new piece not being ready, Carte
had to fill in the gap with revivals of *Trial by Jury* and *The
Sorcerer,* and a children's production of *The Pirates of Penzance*
for matinées.

The lyrical quality of Sullivan's beautiful music might have
carried along a poorer book if the subject had been less controversial, but even such a happy combination of words and music
as the song *Expressive Glances* could not keep the piece playing
beyond October.

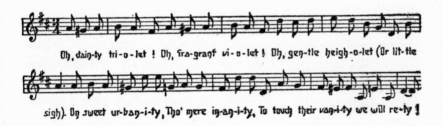

9

FTER *Princess Ida,* many of the most faithful "Savoyards" began to doubt if Gilbert and Sullivan would turn out another opera as good as *H.M.S. Pinafore* or *Patience.* Some of the critics said frankly that they would not. No one knew that Gilbert was already at work on the best opera of all.

The libretto for the most popular of the Savoy Operas was written in the comfortable study at No. 39 Harrington Gardens, South Kensington, the elaborate town house which Gilbert had built for himself in 1883. The playwright had spared no expense. Valuable woods, expensive tiles and marbles had gone into this house of spacious rooms and generous grounds. Gilbert may not have cared for a French chef, but he enjoyed the extravagance of a fine home.

Writing and rewriting the dialogue, jokes, and songs for the story which took its place as number nine of the "golden fourteen," Gilbert sat in his big armchair night after night from eleven o'clock to four. Those were the hours when he did his best work, for, as he explained, "No one can interrupt you unless it be a burglar."

Gilbert was fond of telling how the idea of this ninth opera came to him. While he was at work in his study one day, only half his brain busy with the task at hand, the other half worrying at the problem of what might please Sullivan in the composer's difficult new mood, one of the souvenirs which decorated the walls fell with a clatter. It was not one of the small stage properties nor one of the numerous autographed pictures of actors and actresses, but a large samurai sword from the then mysterious land of Nippon, the Japanese land of the shogun, the geisha, and the Mikado.

The Mikado! Walking over to replace the heavy sword, Gilbert forgot the papers on his desk. Images very unlike the fairy queens, pirate captains, and pale poets and curates of earlier ballads, plays, and operas trooped into his mind. He was seeing quaint tea gardens with quiet pools where water lilies floated, half-round bridges and tiny women in bright kimonos, lanterns swinging in a gentle breeze, crickets in a willow cage, and glowworms in the grass. Torii gates and snow-capped Fujiyama painted on scrolls and delicate silk screens were part of this bizarre dream, and the drums and sounding brass gongs of strange music in the Oriental six-note scale.

Why, thought Gilbert, coming to himself with a start, what he was actually seeing in his mind's eye was Knightsbridge! In this little village just outside London, a colony of Japanese had settled. They had built picturesque tea gardens and dainty shops for the amusement of Londoners, who came by the thousands on Sundays and holidays to wonder at the strange ways of the little people from the "land of the rising sun." For the Victorians of the eighties, Knightsbridge was a mildly exotic adventure in Oriental culture. Drinking tea out of porcelain bowls, eating rice with chopsticks, buying fans, parasols, and lacquer boxes from native Japanese craftsmen at work in the little shops—all this was part of the interest in the "pretty-pretty" side of Japan which had become almost a mania since 1853, the year that Commodore Perry and four United States warships delivered a letter to the Mikado and induced Japan to open her door to extensive foreign trade.

Turning the sword over and over in his hands, Gilbert smiled wryly to himself. Here he stood, finding romance and inspiration in a theatrical little village of plaster Buddhas and artificial cherry blossoms, and just three operas ago (*Patience*) he had been poking sarcastic fun at the long-haired poet with the Japanese mania, calling him

> "A Japanese young man
> A blue-and-white young man."

Gilbert, the foe of manias, fads, and crazes, had held up to ridicule all who professed a mad passion for

> ". . . all one sees
> That's Japanese."

Having rehung the sword, Gilbert hurried back to his desk. *The Mikado*. That would be the name of his new opera. He would give London something every bit as Japanese as—well, as Knightsbridge! Sullivan should have his "story of human interest and probability." Probability? Well, at least there would be no lozenges, love philters, or fairy queens.

A wicked gleam lighted up Gilbert's shrewd eyes as he began the outline of his new plot. If you think for one moment that Babs-Ballad Gilbert was intending to write a realistic libretto, or a sweet, sentimental story all about innocent little geishas, noble samurai, generous shoguns, and a gracious Mikado so dazzling that to look upon his divine splendor was to court blindness, then, to quote the opening chorus of the Japanese story which Gilbert *did* write,

"If that's your idea, you're wrong, oh!"

No indeed! Gilbert, who lived in a Topsy-Turvy Land of his own, had another plan. His characters would pose on the stage in gorgeous robes and fetching kimonos. They would strike attitudes "queer and quaint" like those

"On many a vase and jar—
     On many a screen and fan."

But as soon as they began to go about their business and opened up their mouths to pass the time of day with their neighbors— then it would be clear that they were only English men and women at a sort of Oriental masquerade, playing at being Japanese.

This would be the fun of the thing, thought Gilbert. First, fool the audience. Give them an exotic stage picture, a palace court-yard with Japanese nobles holding enormous fans and wearing robes of silver and black, gold and green, amber and blue. Have them sitting and standing in attitudes suggested by native brush drawings. Then, into the midst of this throng, introduce a beautiful Japanese young man singing:

"A wandering minstrel I—
     A thing of shreds and patches,
     Of ballads, songs, and snatches,
And dreamy lullaby!"

And then, with the audience sitting in open-mouthed wonder at the Japanese charm of the thing—off with the masks! On stage, Ko-Ko the Tailor, Lord High Executioner of Titipu! Your cue, Pooh-Bah, Lord High Everything Else! Your cue to explain, "I am, in point of fact, a particularly haughty and exclusive person, of pre-Adamite ancestral descent . . . my family pride is something inconceivable. I can't help it. I was born sneering . . ."

Where's your Japanese charm now, you funny Londoners who go to Knightsbridge? You know Pooh-Bah only too well. In spite of his kimono sleeves and his fan, he lives in England, sometimes at No. 10 Downing Street. He carries a cane or an umbrella instead of a fan, but he's old Pooh-Bah just the same.

It was Gilbert's mission to say that under shimmering silks or coarse woolen stuff, people are people. No matter what face they present to the world, under the masks are vanity and ego, timidity and cowardice, selfishness and greed and cruelty, too. And, of course, genuine sentiment, kindliness, humor, and nobility. This is a fact, said Gilbert, and

"You're wrong if you think it ain't, oh!"

You are also wrong if you think that Gilbert, flushed with inspiration, took up his pen and dashed off the two acts of *The Mikado* at one sitting. Oh, no. That was not Gilbert's way. He was a careful, methodical worker, who wrote out his story as many as twelve times before the synopsis pleased him. An English country gentleman going over his steward's reports, or a solicitor writing an unimaginative brief for a minor case—Gilbert might have sat for either portrait as he worked doggedly away at his fanciful make-believe.

When *The Mikado* in brief narrative form, without dialogue, lyrics, or jokes, suited him at last, Gilbert rolled up his manuscript.

put on his overcoat, and marched like a general over to Sullivan's flat. They dined together, and afterwards Gilbert read his story aloud.

Sullivan's tired face lighted up with pleasure. The composer was aware that he was listening to the reading of an almost perfect comic-opera plot. The characterizations were good. The comedy grew naturally out of the action. The plot had verve. There was a considerable amount of dramatic suspense building up to a real climax. Above all, there was beauty in the story—the beauty which lies in youth itself, in tenderness and pathos, and good, wholesome humor. And there was satiric wit, like bright steel gleaming amid silken folds.

The composer was aware of the story's possibilities for gay and brilliant music before the reading was halfway through. Good old Gilbert had done it again. He had struck just the right tone, and Sullivan's musical genius responded in the old way.

Gilbert sensed his partner's pleasure, and sighed with relief as he sat back to listen to Sullivan's enthusiastic comments and suggestions. This is the way they always worked when they were in harmony. Every suggested change made by the composer was noted down and usually accepted without debate; for it was part of Gilbert's greatness that he recognized in Sullivan an artist with perfect taste and unerring instinct for symmetry and balance. In this respect, as well as in his gift of melody, Sullivan's artistic kinship with Mozart revealed itself.

Following the first reading, Gilbert revised the story once more, and then he set to work to write the book in dramatic form, that is to say, in dialogue, with the narrative reduced to terse stage directions. There were no jokes or songs in this version, which was written and rewritten until Gilbert had satisfied himself that the action of the story had been carried forward in the fewest possible words. Gilbert was a firm believer in the old axiom that brevity is the soul of wit.

Once he was satisfied with the bare bones of his dialogue, Gilbert turned to the songs. Being a practical man of the theater, he timed his songs and dialogue in relation to each other with a nice appreciation of what was dramatic, and calculated the intervals at which the lyrics should interrupt the action with the precision of a mathematician. As for the songs themselves, they were little gems of humor and gayety and shrewd philosophy.

With the songs out of the way, Gilbert returned to the dialogue and rounded it out with jokes, or "gags" as they would be called today. These jokes, like the songs, were placed and timed with careful attention to the dramatic value of the scene. That is why Gilbert objected strenuously whenever an actor tried to insert a joke or piece of business of his own.

The story is told of Grossmith that during a performance of one of the operas, in an earnest but mistaken desire to improve a funny scene, he fell over and rolled on the floor. This piece of business in no way furthered the action of the play, nor grew logically out of the story.

"Kindly omit that fall, Grossmith," said Gilbert sternly to the actor after the show.

Grossmith, somewhat crestfallen, agreed to omit the fall, but pointed out, in a sudden burst of spirit, that the audience had laughed.

"They would have laughed if you'd sat on a pork pie," commented Gilbert.

It was sometime about May 8th when the Japanese sword fell in Gilbert's study, and yet six months later a note in Sullivan's diary mentions that he dined with Gilbert and his wife and discussed Act One, which was "still in an incomplete and somewhat crude condition . . . Some words for music ready."

Between November 20th and March 14th, Sullivan did his part of the work. He was slow, as usual, in getting started. A month passed before he began to compose the first music for the opera— *Three Little Maids from School.*

Unlike Gilbert, Sullivan was not a plodding worker. Periods of inertia, which drove the methodical Gilbert to distraction, gave way to periods of furious energy and inspiration. Thus it was that the music for the *Three Little Maids* and a quintet were completed in one day, December 21st, after a full month of marking time. Again one sees the remarkable resemblance to Mozart, who had to be locked in his room to write his music for *The Magic Flute.*

All of January found the composer depressed and unable to work. News had reached him of his sister-in-law's death in Los Angeles, California. He fell to worrying over his brother's children, left motherless. Consoling himself somewhat with the thought that he would visit them when the opera was finished, he forced himself back to work.

Time was distressingly short. As usual, Sullivan had so put off the task to be done that he had to drive himself at a killing pace to meet the deadline. During February, he worked from dusk to dawn every night. Between February 21st and March 1st, he did not leave his rooms at Queen's Mansions once, except to attend the music rehearsals at the Savoy. On March 3rd, he laid down his pen at five in the morning and noted in his diary, "63 pages of score at one sitting!" One week before the opening night, Sullivan's completed score was in Carte's hands.

While Sullivan was working feverishly on the music score,

Gilbert was no less feverishly rehearsing the Savoy company. The disappointment of *Princess Ida* rankled. The new opera must be a success, he told himself, and if perfect costuming and set-designing, and flawless acting could be achieved, they would go a long way toward insuring that success.

The best costume designers of the day were hired to clothe the cast, and a few really priceless garments from old Japan were added to the wardrobe. Not content with what *he* thought Japanese men and women should look and act like, Gilbert went straight to Knightsbridge, hired experts to come to the Savoy and coach the cast in the proper Japanese etiquette of holding fans, of walking, of giggling, of doing hair, and a hundred other matters.

Gilbert drilled the company until they were ready to drop from weariness, and then drilled them some more. Every gesture, every step, every facial expression was rehearsed over and over again, and woe to the poor player who made even the slightest deviation from the business decided upon. Gilbert had nothing but Almond-Rock days during the rehearsals, so it seemed to the distracted principals and brow-beaten chorus. Gilbert was proving himself a disagreeable man indeed, and his actors, unlike King Gama, could have thought of any number of reasons why.

Once in a while Gilbert dropped his savage driving for a more playful, though not a kinder mood. The story is told that a new girl joined the chorus. Not knowing Gilbert's irascible temper, she disturbed him during a rehearsal by running up to report that one of the men of the chorus had put his arm around her waist and called her a "pretty dear." Gilbert looked the little singer up and down, and said wickedly, "Never mind, never mind. He couldn't have meant it."

Gilbert made the cast suffer, but it must be confessed that he suffered even more. On the evening of the first performance of *The Mikado* he was scurrying about back stage like a mother hen with one chick. In and out of dressing rooms he popped, begging the nervous actors to remember their lines, reminding them of weak points, urging them to do their best. They, poor souls, had to go on with the show, no matter what the state of their nerves. Gilbert could go away, and he did. Before the curtain went up, he was wandering the streets of London.

Gilbert's courage was never equal to a performance of one of his operas. The dress rehearsal was as near as he ever came to seeing one of his own shows.

Sullivan arrived on the big night calm and serene. Nervous and excitable during the creative part of his work, the composer was always self-possessed and smiling when he took his place in the orchestra pit. His poise did much to offset the nervous tension which was Gilbert's sole contribution to a first night. The opening performance of *The Mikado* was no exception. Orchestral players and singers alike looked at the kindly little man with the baton and took heart.

But now the house lights are dimming. The curtain is about to go up on the opera which played at the Savoy for six hundred consecutive nights. The conductor raises his baton. With a brilliance that sets every nerve to tingling, the smashing opening notes of the Overture sound. There is vigor and dash in this music, a kind of breathless excitement that brings a flush to the listener's cheek and makes him conscious of his heartbeat. This is *The Mikado* and it's worth listening to, the Overture is saying.

The last vivacious notes have hardly sounded when up goes the curtain on a scene which brings the first-night audience to its feet

The Mikado

with prolonged cheers and cries of delight. The scene: Ko-Ko's palace in Titipu. The stage picture is like a beautiful silk screen. Fujiyama, wreathed in clouds, in the distance. At hand, an exotic Japanese courtyard. Through an impressive gateway at the top of a flight of steps, a glimpse of the street beyond. As if painted on this background, kimono-clad noblemen with topknots and gorgeous fans stand or sit in stiff attitudes.

Suddenly the scene comes to life. The deep voices of the male chorus sing the vigorous lines:

> "If you want to know who we are,
>   We are gentlemen of Japan."

When the last prolonged "Oh!" of this song has floated over the wall to distant Fujiyama, Nanki-Poo, dressed as a street musician, enters the courtyard and asks for news of Yum-Yum, ward of Ko-Ko. When the nobles demand to know who *he* is, he replies with *A wandering minstrel I.* This is a graceful song, with just the right plaintiveness in the opening stanzas to describe the lover's longing. It changes mood and struts with a patriotic ballad in mock-heroic vein, and finally swaggers with a song of the sea. For this chantey-type song Sullivan gave Gilbert's words a perfect setting.

Having explained who he is (after a fashion, for we shall soon learn that he has revealed only part of his story), Nanki-Poo tells how he came to fall in love with Yum-Yum, and how, learning that she was betrothed to her guardian, Ko-Ko, he left town in despair. News reached him that Ko-Ko had been condemned to death for the Japanese crime of flirting; so he hurried back to woo Yum-Yum, supposedly free at last.

Pish-Tush, a rather formidable nobleman of the group, dashes his hopes, telling how Ko-Ko escaped his fate to be promoted to the honorable position and title of Lord High Executioner. Some typical Gilbertian logic, which is reason upside-down and hind-side-to, and mocking, tongue-in-cheek music provide Pish-Tush with just the right song to reveal the news he has to tell. He is a conservative gentleman playing safe by endorsing both sides of the question as he explains the ruling Mikado's law that makes flirting a capital crime. His comment on the Mikado's action is:

"And I expect you'll all agree
That he was right to so decree.
    And I am right,
    And you are right,
And all is right as right can be!"

But, says Pish-Tush, strange to say, a person condemned to death under the new law "usually objected," a sentiment with which Pish-Tush also agrees:

"And you'll allow, as I expect,
That he was right to so object.
    And I am right,
    And you are right,
And everything is quite correct!"

And so, he explains, the citizens of Titipu released from the county jail a prisoner who was first on the list of condemned criminals:

"And made *him* Headsman, for we said,
    'Who's next to be decapitated
Cannot cut off another's head
    Until he's cut his own off.'

"And we are right, I think you'll say,
    To argue in this kind of way;
        And I am right,
        And you are right,
    And all is right—too-looral-lay!"

The portly Pooh-Bah enters the scene. He is a nobleman with such a long and aristocratic lineage that his pride is excessive, so he says. But, he hastens to explain, he tries to mortify that pride by working for a living. This "work" consists of accepting all the well-paid government jobs given up by those too proud to take orders from Ko-Ko, a former tailor. As Pooh-Bah says, it is his "degrading duty" to serve the ex-convict and tailor as "First Lord of the Treasury, Lord Chief Justice, Commander-in-Chief, Lord High Admiral, Master of the Buckhounds, Groom of the Back Stairs, Archbishop of Titipu, and Lord Mayor, both acting and elect, all rolled into one. And at a salary! A Pooh-Bah paid for his services! I a salaried minion! But I do it! It revolts me, but I do it!"

And that is not all he does to mortify his pride, says Pooh-Bah. He also retails State secrets for a price, and takes petty bribes of all kinds. The Pooh-Bahs sitting in the Savoy boxes squirmed uncomfortably and smiled at each other rather foolishly.

Having explained just what sort of person he is, Pooh-Bah proceeds to advise Nanki-Poo, in song, to give up all ideas of winning Yum-Yum. Pooh-Bah gets quite intoxicated with his own eloquence, and almost forgets his dignity as he dances a few steps to the playful little tune for

"She'll toddle away, as all aver
    With the Lord High Executioner!"

Nanki-Poo is broken-hearted. As soon as he has told the audience he is, the chorus of nobles announces majestically in song that the Lord High Executioner is about to appear. Carrying his headsman's ax over his shoulder, Ko-Ko, an absurd little man, rather bewildered by his sudden change in fortune, tells his story in song, concluding with:

> "Surely never had a male
>   Under such like circumstances
> So adventurous a tale
>   Which may rank with most romances."

Underneath his clownish exterior, one feels that he is a kindly and timid soul, and that all this should never have happened to him. However, since it has, he is doing his best to carry his honors with dignity, and even to bring mild humor to bear on the case. His song about the list of those people who could best be spared if "some day . . . a victim must be found" is one of the famous songs of *The Mikado*. Following this listing of those who'd "none of 'em be missed!" Ko-Ko consults Pooh-Bah about plans for the approaching marriage to Yum-Yum.

Gilbert's sharp satire was seldom more biting than in this ruthless exposé of pluralism (the holding of many public offices by one person). Pooh-Bah, as he has already revealed, has a great number of high offices in Titipu's government, and Ko-Ko consults him in each of his public rôles. Pooh-Bah tells Ko-Ko that in his capacity of Private Secretary, he advises an expensive wedding. After all, the *public* will have to pay for it. *But*—here Ko-Ko's beaming face clouds—as Chancellor of the Exchequer, he must insist on strict economy. *However*—here Ko-Ko perks up a bit—as Ko-Ko's solicitor, he doesn't hesitate to advise his client to take a chance and go ahead with an expensive wedding. *Still*—poor Ko-Ko looks unhappy again—as Lord Chief Justice, he will not tolerate anything not strictly open and aboveboard. He goes on, first raising then dashing Ko-Ko's hopes, with one of the wittiest speeches in all Gilbert and Sullivan:

"Of course, as First Lord of the Treasury, I could propose a special vote that would cover all expenses, if it were not that, as Leader of the Opposition, it would be my duty to resist it, tooth and nail. Or, as Paymaster-General, I could so cook the accounts that, as Lord High Auditor, I should never discover the fraud. But then, as Archbishop of Titipu, it would be my duty to denounce my dishonesty and give myself into my own custody as First Commissioner of Police."

Having thus convinced Ko-Ko that the case is hopeless, he lowers his voice and suggests that there is one way out. "I don't say that all these distinguished people couldn't be squared," he says, and Ko-Ko sighs with relief. Of course! For an instant he had forgotten about the State secrets and petty bribes. In the audience there were some uncomfortable politicians. A guilty conscience needs no accuser.

Ko-Ko and Pooh-Bah go off together to attend to the bribes and other matters, and the sisters Yum-Yum, Peep-Bo, and Pitti-Sing enter with a chorus of schoolgirls. After the introductory song by the chorus, Yum-Yum and her two sisters sing the demure *Three Little Maids from School,* which has always been a favorite of Savoyards. The audience at the Savoy first-night performance applauded the expert use of the fans which the singers had learned from their Japanese tutors, along with a mincing walk, and the odd hissing sound which is the Japanese equivalent of giggling.

Ko-Ko and Pooh-Bah reënter, and there is a delightful, frolic-

some scene in which the schoolgirls make sport of the pompous
old aristocrat. Their song of half-serious, half-mocking apology
is gay and youthful:

> "So please you, sir, we much regret
> If we have failed in etiquette
> Towards a man of rank so high—
> We shall know better by and by.
> But youth, of course, must have its fling,
>> So pardon us,
>> So pardon us,
> If we're inclined to dance and sing.
>> Tra la la, etc."

Everyone dances out, leaving Yum-Yum alone. Nanki-Poo wanders into the courtyard, and there is a romantic meeting, with
avowals of love by Yum-Yum and the minstrel, and sighs and
tears over Ko-Ko, who has spoiled everything for them.

Nanki-Poo tells Yum-Yum that he is really the son of the
Mikado. He ran away from his father's Court and disguised himself as a street musician to escape marrying a terrifying old lady,
Katisha, who mistook his courtesy for flirting and demanded that
he marry her or lose his head.

During this scene, both Yum-Yum and Nanki-Poo are pain-
fully aware that flirting is a capital crime. They stay some distance away from each other, maintaining the strictest decorum
until Nanki-Poo hits on the idea of showing Yum-Yum how he
would act if she were *not* betrothed to Ko-Ko. No one can object
to his acting out what he himself would never do. A dainty,
whimsical duet follows, in which they kiss behind Yum-Yum's fan
and sing:

"Let me make it clear to you
This is what I'll never do!
This, ah, this, oh, this, oh, this—"

The two lovers leave the stage, sadly going in opposite directions. Ko-Ko enters just in time to meet Pish-Tush, who brings a letter from his Majesty the Mikado! Poor Ko-Ko reads the message and nearly faints. The Mikado is on his way to Titipu. The little tailor jumps to the conclusion that he is coming to check up on the executions. If there are none to report, the whole city will be punished.

Ko-Ko discusses the situation with both Pooh-Bah and Pish-Tush, who are agreed that unless he can find a substitute, there is nothing for it but for him to execute himself, since he is first on the list of criminals. Ko-Ko points out that he cannot decapitate himself, "Because, in the first place, self-decapitation is an extremely difficult, not to say dangerous, thing to attempt . . ."

Pooh-Bah and Pish-Tush decline with thanks the invitation to substitute their necks for his and go away, leaving Ko-Ko wringing his hands. Nanki-Poo enters with an enormous rope. He announces that he intends to put an end to his miserable existence. This gives Ko-Ko an idea. Here is a substitute! He proposes that instead of hanging himself, Nanki-Poo allow Ko-Ko to behead him properly at a later date. Meanwhile, Nanki-Poo will be given every luxury and pleasure there is to be had in Titipu.

This gives Nanki-Poo an idea. He will consent to be beheaded only if Ko-Ko will allow Yum-Yum to be his wife for a month before the execution. Ko-Ko refuses indignantly.

Nanki-Poo refuses to yield ground. No Yum-Yum, suicide at once! he threatens. Marriage to Yum-Yum, public execution in a

month and Ko-Ko's head saved. That is his proposition. Ko-Ko
may take it or leave it. Ko-Ko takes it.

The Lord High Executioner's song with its absurd reasoning
and frank admission of self-interest is a delightful little dig at
fragile humanity, most of which would rather dream about deeds
of derring-do than do them:

> "He yields his life if I'll Yum-Yum surrender.
> Now, I adore that girl with passion tender,
> And could not yield her with a ready will,
>   Or her allot
>   If I did not
> Adore myself with passion tenderer still!"

As for the three little maids, their curiosity having got the better
of them, they creep into the scene, followed by their girl friends
and the various noblemen of Titipu. Nanki-Poo and Yum-Yum
congratulate each other on the solution of their problem with the
delightful song:

> "The threatened cloud has passed away,
> And brightly shines the dawning day;
> What though the night may come too soon,
> There's yet a month of afternoon!"

Everyone catches their devil-may-care mood, even Pooh-Bah, who
proposes a toast to Nanki-Poo. The stage is a lively picture of
bright kimonos, opening and closing fans, and dancing slippered
feet until a veritable bellow announces the arrival of Katisha.

The dancers freeze into immobility while the terrible Katisha
states that she has arrived with the Mikado to seek her runaway
lover, Nanki-Poo. She turns her fierce eyes on the young lovers,

who are doing their best to achieve invisibility. She snarls first at Nanki-Poo, "Oh, fool, that fleest!" Then at Yum-Yum:

"Thy doom is nigh,
Pink cheek, bright eye!
Thy knell is rung,
Rose lip, smooth tongue!"

The chorus, for the moment overawed, tell Yum-Yum, "Thy knell is rung!" But Pitti-Sing, who has had enough of this nonsense, pertly tells Katisha that she will not be allowed to have her way, and the chorus, gaining courage, endorse her views with the sprightly *For he's going to marry Yum-Yum.*

At this point, Katisha seeks full revenge by threatening to tell everyone that Nanki-Poo is the son of the Mikado, but Nanki-Poo and Yum-Yum desperately lead the chorus in a wild song to make the old woman's words unintelligible. With "O ni! bikkuri shakkuri to!" the act closes on the truly Oriental tones of the Eastern six-note scale. Katisha's furious face and menacing, clutching hands as she rushes through the crowd to turn like an enraged tigress at the top of the steps give a strangely sinister turn to the light-hearted make-believe.

Gilbert has often been accused of being something of a cad in respect to aging ladies. In almost every opera, he held up some silly old woman to merciless ridicule. What he found most repulsive was an older woman trying to appear young, especially if her purpose was to ensnare some youthful male. The playwright was almost savage about it, so much so that one wonders if he himself had some unpleasant experience in his youth.

In his zeal to expose the ugliness of such women, Gilbert often overstepped the bounds of good taste. With Ruth of *The Pirates*

of Penzance, it seems as if the silly old girl might have been put
in her place without all the melodrama. Though Lady Jane of
Patience is certainly hysterical and foolish, one feels that it was not
exactly "cricket" to dwell on her fading physical charms.

Katisha is the one such character that does not offend. She is
ugly, through and through. She is vengeful and "tough as a bone."
She is a kind of Greek fury, and she should be banished to the
shadows. When she enters a scene, a cloud obscures the sun and
youthful laughter is stilled. Katisha is ugly passion and remorse-
less selfishness personified. Gilbert wrought better than he knew
when he created Katisha, and Sullivan supplied him music worthy
of his creation. One may feel merely contemptuous of stupid
Ruth, perhaps a little sorry for lovelorn Lady Jane—but Katisha?
Off with her head!

The intermission is over, and the curtain rises on a scene which
makes our Victorian audience catch its breath with pleased surprise. It is Ko-Ko's garden, with a bamboo-and-paper house at one
side, a weeping willow dipping its branches into a pool at the back,
and meandering paths bordered with spring flowers. Yum-Yum
is kneeling before a little table on which are various toilet articles.
Her sisters and bridesmaids are dressing her hair, while she surveys
the effect in a hand mirror. As the bridesmaids work, they sing
a sprightly song to the pretty bride-to-be.

Yum-Yum is not slow to agree with the girls' compliments.
She remarks, "Sometimes I sit and wonder, in my artless Japanese
way, why it is that I am so much more attractive than anybody
else in the whole world. Can it be vanity?"

She answers her own question with a song for which Sullivan
wrote such exquisite and poignant music that it is hard to realize
that the words are essentially comical. In fact, Gilbert's words for
this lyric play tricks on the ear. They lure the listener into believ-

ing them chaste and demure, and then startle him by their impudent sauciness, like a dancer in the midst of a classically beautiful figure suddenly flipping her petticoats in a naughty French can-can. Sullivan, with that understanding which made him the perfect partner for Gilbert, realized that the joke would be all the richer if the music maintained its classic symmetry throughout.

This song of Yum-Yum's on her wedding day never fails to cast its spell:

> "The sun, whose rays
> Are all ablaze
>   With ever-living glory,
> Does not deny
> His majesty—
>   He scorns to tell a story!
> He don't exclaim,
> 'I blush for shame,
>   So kindly be indulgent.'
> But, fierce and bold,
> In fiery gold,
>   He glories all effulgent!
>
>> I mean to rule the earth,
>>   As he the sky—
>> We really know our worth,
>>   The sun and I!
>
> "Observe his flame,
> That placid dame,
>   The moon's Celestial Highness;
> There's not a trace

Upon her face
  Of diffidence or shyness:
She borrows light
That, through the night,
  Mankind may all acclaim her!
And truth to tell,
She lights up well,
  So I, for one, don't blame her!

    Ah, pray make no mistake,
      We are not shy;
    We're very wide awake,
      The moon and I!"

The bride's smiles are turned to tears, however, when she is re-
minded that her husband-to-be will be beheaded in a month.
Nanki-Poo and Pish-Tush enter the garden, and both try to comfort her. Determined to be as brave as Nanki-Poo himself, Yum-
Yum dries her tears and joins him and Pish-Tush and Pitti-Sing
in a madrigal, a song so typically old English in spirit that one
feels that, like Chatterton's poetry, it *might* have been composed
at the time of *Sumer is icumen in.*

Nanki-Poo and Yum-Yum are left together for a moment, only
to be burdened with Ko-Ko's unwelcome presence. He dumb-
founds the two lovers by telling them that, in accordance with the
Mikado's law, when a man is beheaded, his wife must be buried
alive.

Yum-Yum is appalled and promptly breaks off her engagement.
Nanki-Poo is dazed. Ko-Ko is secretly pleased. They plunge into
the amusing trio *Here's a how-de-do!*

It is Ko-Ko's turn to be excited, however, when Nanki-Poo de-

clares his intention of returning to his original plan to commit
suicide. While the distracted Ko-Ko is trying to dissuade him, a
messenger arrives to say that the Mikado is at the city gates.

Nanki-Poo, taking pity on Ko-Ko, says, "Oh, well, go ahead.
Chop my head off."

Ko-Ko, face to face with the harsh realities of his position,
breaks down and weeps and confesses that he cannot kill a fly.
He pulls himself together, however, and proposes another plan.
Why not make an affidavit saying that Nanki-Poo has been beheaded, and have it sworn to by Pooh-Bah in all his capacities?

Having mortified his pride with a suitable bribe, Pooh-Bah cer-
tifies the statement prepared by Ko-Ko. The little tailor in a fit of
generosity tells Nanki-Poo that he may marry Yum-Yum anyway,
if he will just go away at once and pretend to be dead. The lovers
run out happily.

With sound of drum and clang of brass, the Mikado's approach
is announced in the one song which is a real Japanese tune. Sullivan found it somewhere, and adapted it to his purposes. He must
not have bothered his head about what kind of song it was, for he
was amazed, some months after the opera was launched, to have a
very agitated Japanese gentleman seek him out and express horrified surprise over the *Miya sama* song, which he insisted was the
most vulgar song to come out of the opium dens of Nippon.

The composer was considerably disturbed, but did not remove
the song. After all, the words were meaningless to an English
audience, if indeed they were even Japanese. As for the tune, it was
Sullivan's firm belief that music alone would not convey improper
thoughts. He once said: ". . . sounds alone (apart from articulate
words, spectacle, or descriptive programme) must, from their in-
definite nature, be innocent."

The Mikado in all his regal splendor enters in company with
Katisha. They sing a duet in which the monarch announces that

> "In a fatherly kind of way
>   I govern each tribe and sect,
> All cheerfully own my sway—"

But Katisha breaks in to complete the rhyme with her own version
of who is boss:

> "Except his daughter-in-law elect!
>   As tough as a bone,
>   With a will of her own,
> Is his daughter-in-law elect!"

There follows the famous song of the Mikado, in which he tells
his people that

> "My object all sublime
> I shall achieve in time—
> To let the punishment fit the crime—
>   The punishment fit the crime;
>   And make each prisoner pent
>   Unwilling represent
> A source of innocent merriment!
>   Of innocent merriment!"

The Mikado having described in detail the various sadistic punishments he has devised for certain persons with irritating habits,
Pooh-Bah, Ko-Ko, and Pitti-Sing enter and present the certificate
of death. Somewhat taken aback when their "humane Mikado"
demands to hear all the gruesome details of the supposed beheading, they rally quickly and sing him some highly colored versions

of how "The criminal cried, as he dropped him down" and of the "shriek that shrieked he."

This report pleases the monarch, but he says that, though it has been most interesting, he is more concerned with another matter. He has come to seek his runaway son, Nanki-Poo. At that moment, Katisha reads Nanki-Poo's name in the faked death certificate, and utters a terrible cry.

All is consternation when the trio realize that they have just presented convincing proof of the execution of the heir to the throne of Japan. They fall in abject attitudes and explain that they had no idea who Nanki-Poo really was. The Mikado is sympathetic, says of course, how could they know?—and then dashes their hope of pardon by saying that the law decreeing death for those who murder a prince has nothing in it about mistakes and not knowing. There is no way out. Ko-Ko, Pooh-Bah, and Pitti-Sing must pay the penalty for their zeal—after luncheon.

After singing a neat little song about the perversity of fate, which punishes the innocent and lets the wicked go free, the Mikado and Katisha leave the stunned trio. Nanki-Poo and Yum-Yum, who have just been married, enter. Ko-Ko pleads with Nanki-Poo to come to life, but the minstrel refuses on the grounds that Katisha will immediately demand his death. There is a possible way out, however. If Ko-Ko will woo and win the formidable Katisha, she will have no claim on Nanki-Poo. Then he will return and be as gay as "the flowers that bloom in the spring."

Katisha enters as they leave and sings her genuinely pathetic *Hearts do not break!* For a moment as she sings, "May not a cheated maiden die?" one is inclined to feel sorry for her—but only for a moment. Next thing you know, she is back to her old vengeful spirit, and little Ko-Ko, who enters on his wooing mission, is the one who wins our pity.

Ko-Ko pleads with Katisha to marry him, and by way of telling her how much her love means to him, sings the famous *On a tree by a river a little tom-tit.*

The song accomplishes its purpose. Katisha consents to the marriage. The two sing an incomparable duet, the music of which is a rollicking dance tune:

> "If that is so,
> Sing derry down derry!"

From this point on, matters move to a swift climax. Nanki-Poo presents himself with his bride, to the consternation of the thwarted Katisha. The Mikado is none too pleased about the deception practiced upon him, but Ko-Ko gets himself and his companions neatly out of trouble by explaining that the fairy tale which they made up for the Mikado was not such a fairy tale, after all.

"It's like this," he says. "When your Majesty says, 'Let a thing be done,' it's as good as done . . . Your Majesty says, 'Kill a gentleman!' . . . that gentleman is as good as dead—practically, he *is* dead—and if he is dead, why not say so?"

There is no answering *that* kind of logic; so the Mikado decides that "Nothing could be more satisfactory!"

Everyone is happy in Titipu. The people burst into the joyful song, "For he's gone and married Yum-Yum—Yum-Yum!" And the opera ends with the merry invitation:

> "Then let the throng
> Our joy advance
> With laughing song
> And merry dance."

When the final curtain shuts away the light-hearted singing and dancing, the audience rises, heads ringing with the many sprightly songs. Which is best? Impossible to choose one, of course, among so many gems. And yet—

There is one song which has a way of coming to mind first. This is Ko-Ko's ballad which wins old Katisha. Gilbert's clever words are here, as in the other comic songs, carefully chosen to make us laugh, but there is something delicate and wistful, too, in the general effect, a something which Sullivan caught and preserved in his plaintive little tune. The result is a comic song with a touch of pathos which makes it indescribably winsome:

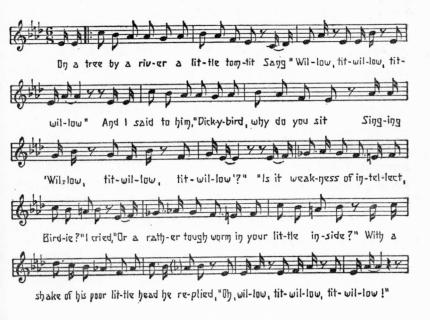

On a tree by a riv-er a lit-tle tom-tit Sang "Wil-low, tit-wil-low, tit-wil-low" And I said to him, "Dick-y-bird, why do you sit Sing-ing 'Wil-low, tit-wil-low, tit-wil-low'?" "Is it weak-ness of in-tel-lect, Bird-ie?" I cried, "Or a rath-er tough worm in your lit-tle in-side?" With a shake of his poor lit-tle head he re-plied, "Oh, wil-low, tit-wil-low, tit-wil-low!"

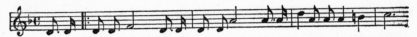

When the night wind howls in the chim-ney cowls, and the bat in the moon-light flies,

10

THE SUCCESS of *The Mikado* was a tonic for both Gilbert and Sullivan. Sullivan particularly was released from nagging care and uncertainty. Three months after seeing the opera off to a good start, he sailed once more for America. He was keeping the promise made to himself during the weeks of hard work on the opera, to see his brother's children, left motherless in the far-off Western state of California.

Carte had sailed just before him, but his mission was purely business. Word had reached him that a manager named Duff was getting ready to put on a pirated version of *The Mikado* in New York. It was Carte's intention to put on an authorized version, and at least seriously hurt Duff's business even if he could not prevent the rival show from opening.

Sullivan stopped for only a few days in New York before he took train for the West. For a man who had spent most of his life in London, among wealthy people and in luxurious surroundings at that, the trip was like an adventure in pioneering. His diary soon contained many vivid impressions. In Chicago, he was mobbed by reporters, who followed him even into his bedroom at the hotel

186

where he stopped, and interviewed him while he undressed. For a reserved Englishman, this was an inexcusable breach of privacy. Aggressive American journalism was something which he could not accept with his usual good humor. He fled to Denver.

The grandeur of the snow-clad Rockies filled him with awe as his train made its way toward Grand Junction, Colorado, on the western slope, and thence to Salt Lake City. The passengers of the train were held up for a whole day near Grand Junction because an engine had smashed through a bridge. There was no food on the train. Sullivan along with the rest of the passengers did without.

In Salt Lake City he was met by an old friend, who drove him to the spots of principal interest. The Mormons fascinated Sullivan. His diary records his seeing the Brigham Young family, visiting the Zion Coöperative Stores, and playing for an hour on the great organ in the Tabernacle. The next day he went to a service in the Tabernacle, and was both surprised and pleased that the hymn tune chosen for the occasion was his own arrangement of St. Ann's tune.

When he arrived in San Francisco, he took time to visit Chinatown. In company with a detective, a certain Devitt, whom Sullivan spoke of as "a great character," he went to see a Chinese play and poked his nose inside the door of a few opium dens, of which there were a great number in the eighties.

In Los Angeles, Sullivan found his brother's children in good health, and a little less lonely than they had been immediately after their mother's death. Having satisfied himself that they were comfortable and well cared for, he asked them how they would like a trip to Yosemite.

The trip was just what they needed, Sullivan as well as the

children. The quiet and beauty of the forests, the grandeur of the great falls of water, the wholesome exercise in the cool, fresh air of the mountains worked their healing magic. Long evening and morning strolls through the meadows where deer grazed and little squirrels darted here and there gathering their winter hoard brought color to the children's cheeks. Sullivan, watching them, was glad of the impulse which had brought him all the way across the Atlantic Ocean and clear across the North American continent to be with them.

In August, he said a reluctant goodbye to the little family and started East. He visited several picturesque towns of the Southwest, where he had amusing adventures and felt positively that he was living the life of the old West.

In one such town, he was greeted by an enthusiastic group of men who had been told, perhaps by some practical joker, that he was "Slugger" Sullivan, the pugilist.

One of the men looked at him doubtfully, and asked, "How much do you weigh?" Sullivan was naturally surprised at the question, but answered good-naturedly, "One hundred sixty-two pounds. Why?"

His questioner was even more surprised. How could so light a fighter have won a bout with a certain heavyweight of sports fame! The man spoke his thought aloud, and it was the composer's turn to be astonished. "But I didn't!" he exclaimed. "I've never seen this heavyweight you talk about!"

Light began to dawn. "Who are you, anyway?" the men wanted to know.

"I'm Arthur Sullivan," replied the composer. "Not 'slugger' Sullivan."

A general laugh greeted this revelation. Then the man who had

questioned him first spoke up again. "Not the Sullivan as put
Pinafore together?"

"The same," answered the composer, his eyes twinkling.

"Well, we're just as glad to see you as the Slugger anyway.
Come have a drink."

And Sullivan went merrily with his reception committee to the
rough-and-ready entertainment which they had planned for the
boxer.

At another small town, he was invited to attend a ball at the
home of one of the principal citizens. It was a dismal affair. The
orchestra could not produce music worth dancing to, and the
company could not have danced if they had had good music. Sullivan, who knew none of the crowd, not even his host and hostess,
so informally had the invitation been arranged, tried to hide in a
corner. He tried to think how he could make his escape without
offending anyone.

A man apparently in the same frame of mind came up to him
and offered him a cigar, with the remark, "It's not very lively,
is it?"

"No, it isn't," said Sullivan, smiling. "Let's go!"

"Well, I'd like to, but I can't," his companion confessed. "You
see, I'm giving the ball."

Sullivan was back in New York by the end of September. Carte
met him with the news that their *Mikado* was packing in huge
crowds, and that Duff's performance around the corner was having a hard time to make expenses. A gala performance was arranged, with the fact that Sullivan would conduct widely adver-
tised.

Carte did not believe in doing things by halves. For this occasion, the theater was decked with gorgeous flowers, every woman who attended the show was given a bouquet of flowers, and beautifully decorated programs were presented to the audience.

Sullivan was cheered to the rafters after the show, and he responded with a short speech on the subject of the need for a copyright law to protect performing rights of librettist and composer of works like *The Mikado*. A sympathetic, fair-minded audience applauded his speech. This speech, together with the previous efforts of the trio from England to protect their property from the producer-pirates, undoubtedly laid the groundwork for the fairer laws which the great American composer Victor Herbert and his associates in ASCAP later pushed through Congress.

At the end of October, Sullivan was back in London, pleased with the news that *The Mikado* was likely to run for a long time at the Savoy. The Japanese embassy had been protesting that the opera held the Mikado up to ridicule, but nothing came of their demand to have it banned. Queen Victoria wrote for the music. Massenet sent Sullivan his congratulations, calling him a master. Translated versions were showing in Holland and Berlin. The composer sighed with relief. No need to bother his poor head about another opera just yet!

Gilbert broke into this lazy mood with a proposal that they should get a work ready ahead of time. And, of all things, he proposed the lozenge plot again. Sullivan's patience was at an end. He wrote Gilbert, saying that his opinion of the plot was unchanged. He suggested that Gilbert put the thing away, not just for a short time, but *forever*. Gilbert had the good sense to drop the subject. With the holidays approaching, Gilbert possessed his soul in patience.

With the round of Christmas and New Year's parties out of the

way, Sullivan might be willing to settle down to work, Gilbert
reasoned. On a cold, snowy January day, he put on his heaviest
coat and battled his way through a blizzard to Sullivan's rooms.
The composer greeted him warmly, helped him brush off a mountain of snow, and brought him into a room where a cheery fire
burned, where good drinks stood on a table near at hand, and
good cigars lay in the humidor.

Sullivan kept his fingers crossed. He was sure that only a comic-
opera plot could have brought Gilbert out in such weather. How
he hoped his partner had not brought the old lozenge with him!
Gilbert had not. He had brought instead the idea for a fantastic
but fascinating story laid in Cornwall.

Gilbert gave Sullivan the crude outline of the plot. Sullivan
began to make excited suggestions. His ideas stimulated Gilbert.
They were like two children weaving a fairy tale.

Sullivan's manservant announced that luncheon was ready. He
was impatiently waved away. An hour later, the servant tried his
luck again. Still deep in their "plotting," Gilbert and Sullivan sat
down at the table, hardly tasted their food as they talked steadily
about seafaring men, village damsels, a chorus of ancestors, a
witch's curse, Mad Margaret's dance, the ancestral hall of the
Murgatroyds, and such like matters. When Gilbert left for home,
the story for *Ruddigore* was in the main decided upon, and he had
Sullivan's promise to begin the music just as soon as the composer
had finished a composition for the coming Leeds Festival.

But Sullivan, as usual, had a hard time getting started. February
arrived, and he had not yet decided on a subject for the Leeds
music. Joseph Bennett solved this part of the problem by bringing
Sullivan a libretto of his own based on Longfellow's *The Golden
Legend*. Sullivan paid him three hundred pounds for the dramatic

adaptation—and settled down to do nothing. He did nothing, that is, in the way of composing. He went to the races. He entertained Franz Liszt. He went to smoking concerts of the Royal Amateur Orchestral Society, in which his friend the Duke of Edinburgh led the first violins. In short, he did everything but work.

Gilbert, the fiend for work and the slave of duty, fumed and fretted. He even came to see Sullivan to take him to task for his laziness. Sullivan's diary records that he "gave it to him back." The composer asked Gilbert indignantly if he thought he was a barrel organ that could grind out tunes day or night. And then he promptly took on some more work! He agreed to set an ode of Tennyson's for the forthcoming Colonial and Indian Exposition of the Queen's Jubilee year.

He rented a cottage in Yorktown in the spring. By the end of April, he was at last working on his cantata, *The Golden Legend.* On August 25th, he was finished. It had been hard work, and he was glad it was over. His physical suffering had been intense during this time, too, and the worst of it was, as he wrote his friend Alexander Mackenzie: "Some people suffer and get well again. I suffer and don't."

Early in October, Sullivan was in Leeds rehearsing the cantata. Dvořák of the sad eyes and merry smile was there also, rehearsing *Ludmila.* The two composers drank ale together after working hours, exchanged reminiscences of musical friends, and talked "shop," that musical language which knows no national barriers.

The Golden Legend had some truly beautiful solos and choruses, notably *It is the sea,* and *O Pure in Heart;* but even Sullivan's stanchest admirers were not prepared for the frenzied acclamation which greeted Sullivan at the end of the performance at Leeds. The audence stood up on their chairs and shouted. They waved programs and hats. They showered the composer with bouquets of flowers. When he turned to bow his thanks to the choir, they also pelted him with bouquets which had been previously concealed under their chairs.

Gilbert was just waiting for this moment. He sent a note of congratulation to the composer, saying that the *Legend* appeared to be the biggest thing he had done, and then abruptly suggested that it might be a good idea to begin *Ruddigore*. Sullivan got down to it in November, promising the music for the end of January. The usual frenzied composing and rehearsing went forward, and on the night of January 22nd, the curtain rose on one of the most expensive productions ever seen at the Savoy. Settings and costumes for this opera cost more than eight thousand pounds.

Ruddigore opens in the quaint fishing village of Rederring in Cornwall, in which lived a beautiful maiden whose name was Rose Maybud. Every boy in the countryside was in love with her, but she was such a coy and modest girl, with such a touch-me-not air, that none of them had plucked up courage to ask her hand in marriage. This state of things annoyed a group of village girls who were members of "an endowed corps of professional bridesmaids . . . bound to be on duty every day from ten to four." Not only was the charity which financed them practically wasted if they were never able to be bridesmaids, but also they themselves had no chance of marrying until Rose made her choice.

They finally appealed to Dame Hannah, Rose's aunt, to help them out. Calling her a nice old person, they suggested that she might marry and provide the bridesmaids with employment. Zorah, one of the prettiest and most impatient of the girls, even mentioned the name of a husband. Why not marry old Adam, the faithful servant of a handsome young man called Robin?

Dame Hannah, however, told them that she had long ago taken a vow never to wed. In her youth, she had fallen in love with Sir Roderic Murgatroyd of Ruddigore Castle, but because of a curse on the house of Murgatroyd, marriage had been impossible. The curse had been pronounced on the first baronet, Sir Rupert Murgatroyd, whose hobby had been burning witches at the stake. One of his victims yelled from the flames and smoke, cursing the whole family, saying that henceforth the eldest son of the Murgatroyds of Ruddigore should commit one crime each day, forever. Failing to do so, he would die in agony. Since Hannah could not bring herself to marry a criminal, she had tearfully parted from her beloved baronet, who since had died by his own hand, leaving the castle and the curse to his son, Sir Despard.

Hannah knew that Rose was secretly in love with the handsome farmer Robin. When she suggested that the young lady should encourage her lover, however, Rose primly refused to make the first advance. Rose was addicted to reading a book of etiquette. Her conduct was shaped according to the prudish rules within its covers, and these forbade any frank and honest approach to love.

After this conversation between Hannah and Rose, Robin came along. It seemed to him that Rose had never looked so pretty and sweet as she did that morning, tripping daintily along with her book of etiquette and a basket of dainties for the poor. She had "peppermint rock for old gaffer Gadderby, a set of false teeth for pretty Ruth Rowbottom, and a pound of snuff for the poor orphan girl on the hill."

Robin almost found the courage to speak his piece, but not quite. Then the brilliant thought struck him that he would pretend to have a friend in love with a beautiful girl but too shy to propose marriage. Rose entered into the spirit of the game, and gave him advice, saying that if *she* were the maid, she would meet the youth halfway. Robin almost found the courage to speak to her on the strength of that advice, but at the last minute he wilted and meekly said goodbye.

As he walked along, cursing himself for a coward, Robin met his old servant Adam, who told him that Robin's foster-brother Richard, a man-o'-war's man, had just put in to port. In the course of their talk, Adam let slip the fact that Robin was no simple farmer, as he pretended, but actually the real Baronet of Ruddigore, who had run away to avoid falling heir to the curse of the Murgatroyds. Nothing had been heard of him at the castle for so long that he was believed to be dead.

Swashbuckling Richard, surrounded by admiring village girls, sang out a greeting when he caught sight of Robin, and began to tell him a few stories of his adventures on the sea. Noticing that Robin seemed thoughtful, he questioned him closely. Robin, rather glad to tell his troubles, revealed his love for Rose and his lack of courage to tell her of it. Richard offered at once to speak for him.

As soon as the sailor set eyes on Rose, he fell head over heels in love and proposed on his own account. Rose promptly accepted him, to the delight of the bridesmaids, who danced about the couple gleefully and sang, "Hail the bridegroom—hail the bride."

When Robin next met Rose and Richard, he saw at once the true state of things. Heartbroken over the betrayal of his confidence, he spoke out, confessing his love without thought for his former shyness. Without a moment's hesitation, Rose broke off her engagement to Richard and accepted Robin.

A short time later, Rose, still with her basket of goodies, met a strange, unkempt girl dressed in rags. This was Mad Margaret, who lost her reason when she was jilted by Sir Despard, Baronet of Ruddigore. Rose walked along with the poor distraught creature, trying to comfort her. They just missed meeting Sir Despard face to face as he walked into the hamlet.

A merry crowd of village girls and their beaux, handsome young soldiers in gorgeous uniforms, stopped their singing and laughing when they caught sight of the dreadful Baronet. Sir Despard was soon alone in the empty street. Richard came upon him as he strode furiously along, scowling darkly, his eyes stormy with his rebellious thoughts.

Wishing to hurt Robin, Richard informed Sir Despard of the young farmer's true identity. Sir Despard's eyes lighted up with hope. Here at last was a promise of deliverance from the curse. Seeking out Rose and Robin, the Baronet wasted no time in telling them what he had learned. Rose, appalled at the thought of marrying Robin, now exposed as the real Baronet of Ruddigore, turned from him in horror. Quite forgetting her book of etiquette, she offered to marry Sir Despard, but he turned her down, preferring to atone for the wrong he had done Mad Margaret years before. Flighty Rose, realizing that Richard was the only one left, lost no time in completing the circle and accepting him again. During all these changes, the bridesmaids were kept busy singing "Hail the bridegroom—hail the bride!"

Poor Robin, doomed to a life of crime, first tried to make these necessary crimes as harmless as possible. At table, he bit his bread. which, according to Rose's book of etiquette, was a pretty serious crime.

As he walked one night in the hall along which hung the oil

portraits of his ancestors, what was his terror to see all the baronets of Ruddigore stepping out of their frames and approaching him angrily. They demanded that he get down to business and commit a *real* crime. They suggested that carrying off a lady would be all right.

Robin was in the depths of despair. Not even the sight of Despard and Margaret, who came to the castle to tell him of their marriage, could cheer him.

Robin dared not go counter to his ancestors' wishes. He had already made one half-hearted attempt to do so, but the terrible agony of body which was the penalty had discouraged further disobedience. Accordingly, Old Adam was sent off to kidnap a lady.

What was Robin's horror when Adam returned with poor old Hannah, Rose's aunt. Hannah managed to grab a dagger from one of the armed figures lining the baronial hall, and threatened to stab Robin. In terror, Robin called on his Uncle Roderic for help. Stepping down from his frame, Hannah's old lover came to the rescue. Robin explained that he had no intention of molesting Hannah further, and tiptoed out to leave the elderly sweethearts alone.

Suddenly Robin had a startling thought. Roderic had comitted suicide to escape the curse on the house of Murgatroyd. And suicide itself was a crime! That meant that Roderic had commited his crime, after all, and, having lived up to the letter of the requirements, should never have died at all. And that meant only one thing—he was not dead!

So Hannah and her old love were united. Rose had another change of heart, and decided to marry Robin. As for Richard, he consoled himself with one of the bridesmaids. The other girls

paired off with their handsome soldiers. And they all lived happily
ever after.

> "For happy the lily
>   That's kissed by the bee;
> And, sipping tranquilly,
>   Quite happy is he;
> And happy the filly
>   That neighs in her pride;
> But happier than any,
> A pound to a penny,
> A lover is, when he
>   Embraces his bride!"

That is the story, and there never was a more fantastic, topsy-
turvy tale for Sullivan to set to music. The composer, proving
that he could be as perverse and contradictory as the librettist,
liked the plot of *Ruddigore* and wrote for it some of his best
music. Having stubbornly refused to down Gilbert's lozenge, he
threw himself enthusiastically into a story of the supernatural and
decidedly improbable.

The opera got off to a bad start because of its name. It suggested
the vulgar "bloody" which the cultured English abhor. Then there
was the unfortunate song sung by Richard about the British man-
of-war and the French "parley-voo." The French resented the
song. Three Frenchmen challenged Gilbert to a duel over it.
What's more, the English resented it, too. For the first time in the
history of the Gilbert and Sullivan operas, a song was booed.
Though *Ruddigore* was not a failure, as some of the critics
claimed, it was not the success it should have been, and has remained one of the least known of the later Savoy operas.

In *Ruddigore* Gilbert was at his satiric best. In songs like that
for Robin in Act Two, with its refrain

> "Oh! a baronet's rank is exceedingly nice,
> But the title's uncommonly dear at the price!"

he laughed to scorn those with titles and those

> "Whose middle-class lives are embarrassed by wives
> Who long to parade as 'My Lady.'"

Never had the composer displayed so well his ability to catch a
mood, whether of tenderness, jollity, or macabre mirth. Hannah's
Legend has a certain mock-sinister quality that reminds one of
Halloween tales told to wide-eyed children. Rose's *Ballad,* which
begins with the graceful lines:

> "If somebody there chanced to be
> Who loved me in a manner true,
> My heart would point him out to me,
> And I would point him out to you."

has the whimsicality and amusing artificiality which Sullivan
knew how to give to the songs of the Dresden-china girls that
Gilbert liked to put into his librettos.

Robin's and Rose's duet *I know a youth who loves a little maid*
is almost as winning as the *Prithee, pretty maiden* of *Patience,*
which it resembles. The music conveys the idea of youthful bash-
fulness and timid yearning in a way that words alone could
never do.

The humorous pointing up of the bridesmaids' song has always
been a delight to lovers of the subtly comic. For the voices, the
composer gave a little note at the end of the line, "Hail the bride-

groom—hail the bride," which, because it is not part of the key chord, sounds like nothing so much as a derisive aside.

Mad Margaret's ballad *To a garden full of posies* captures that innocent Mozartian mood for which Sullivan became famous. The naïve, deceptively simple melody brings for one moment a certain sincerity and sweetness to this fantastic creation of Gilbert's.

For the duet of Sir Despard and Richard, there is a fanciful orchestral accompaniment, and an incomparable tune for "To shirk the task were fiddle-de-dee!" The tender mood of the *Madrigal* shows Sullivan the master of effective ensemble writing. He wrote music of grace and tranquillity for:

"When the buds are blossoming,
Smiling welcome to the spring,
Lovers choose a wedding day—
Life is love in merry May!"

The composer provided a superb setting for *When the night wind howls in the chimney cowls and the bat in the moonlight flies*. With shimmering notes for the upper strings and brief, plaintive passages for his beloved woodwinds, he gave an eerie quality to the "ghosts' high-noon."

For sheer quaintness, nothing in Gilbert and Sullivan can compare with the duet of Sir Despard and Mad Margaret. A dance tune in the interludes is explained by the singers as being "one of our blameless dances." The haunting melody has a strange fascination.

Gilbert and Sullivan were famous for their patter songs. For *Ruddigore* they wrote a patter trio which is a miracle of clever verse and ingenious musical effects. Anyone who has heard this trio, sung by Robin, Sir Despard, and Mad Margaret, cannot forget the relentless orchestral accompaniment, which rushes the singers along, breathless and almost desperate, to the very end comment of

"This particularly rapid, unintelligible patter
Isn't generally heard, and if it is it doesn't matter."

Hannah's song *There grew a little flower* is tender and tuneful, one of the best of the romantic ballads in the Savoy operas. Hannah is unique in that she is an *attractive* aging lady. The music which Sullivan gave her indicates that he was pleasantly aware of this fact.

There is so much good music to choose from, so many quaint, humorous, and tender lyrics, that it is impossible to choose one song to represent the work. One jolly robust tune has always appealed to audiences enjoying *Ruddigore,* however, and is typical of Gilbert and Sullivan, if not of *Ruddigore* alone. This is Robin's song *My boy, you may take it from me,* a setting for some of Gilbert's opinions about getting ahead in the world, which contain a certain amount of mild cynicism and a good deal of truth:

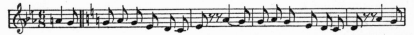

If you wish in the world to ad-vance Your mer-its you're bound to en-hance, You must

Stir it and stump it, And blow your own trum-pet, Or, trust me, you have-n't a chance!

I have a song to sing, O !____   Sing me your song, O !_____

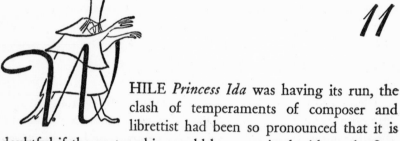

11

HILE *Princess Ida* was having its run, the clash of temperaments of composer and librettist had been so pronounced that it is doubtful if the partnership would have survived without the five-year contract which the two had signed with Carte. The tremendous success of *The Mikado* reconciled Gilbert and Sullivan to working in harness again, but the bond between them was one of business and success. It weakened whenever the box office fell off. The mixed reception of *Ruddigore* renewed the old antagonisms.

The final curtain fell on *Ruddigore*. A new opera was needed. This was in the year 1888. And that was the year that Carte married his brilliant secretary, Miss Helen Lenoir. As an active partner with her husband in the Savoy venture, Mrs. Carte brought her wonderful tact to bear on keeping the peace between Gilbert and Sullivan. Better than anyone else, not even excepting her shrewd and diplomatic husband, she knew how to manage these artists. She knew for one thing that the root of their trouble lay in jealousy, the devastating professional jealousy which is worse than the green-eyed monster of love.

It was almost amusing to see the two great men girding at each other. Each spoke to mutual friends of his grievance against the other, and, as is the way of mutual friends, they saw that the criticisms were promptly repeated where they would do the most harm. Sullivan complained that during rehearsals of *Ruddigore* Gilbert hogged the show, that the piece was made into a play with a few songs and some concerted music. And Gilbert complained that there was too much music, that unless Sullivan agreed to cut his score the audience would lose the thread of the story.

Mrs. Carte spoke separately to each man, praising his work. She wrote little notes to Gilbert, ingeniously worded to soothe his vanity. She and her husband made a point of dining with one or the other to discuss a new opera. But despite all this effort, Sullivan expressed unwillingness to write another opera with Gilbert's inevitable supernatural plot. As he had done just before *The Mikado,* the composer demanded of his librettist a new type of libretto.

Gilbert remained stubborn and sat in his study considering the lozenge. Sullivan turned his back on the squabble and went to Monte Carlo, where he experienced the excitement of an earthquake before he went on to Naples.

In Naples the composer was laid up with a painful attack of his old illness. It was becoming evident that the disease would never give more than temporary peace.

Somehow he mustered the strength to go to Berlin, to attend the festivities connected with the old Emperor William's ninetieth birthday, and to conduct *The Golden Legend* at the Berlin Opera House. Gilbert knew, of course, that the German celebrations were being attended by the English Prince of Wales, and that Sullivan, as usual, was hobnobbing with royalty. The thought brought a sardonic expression to his eyes. He took a grim sort of pleasure in presenting his lozenge to Sullivan once more when the composer returned to England.

The composer sighed, and agreed wearily to set the piece if it appealed to him after more of it was in final form. Then he busied himself with writing music for the Tennyson ode to be played in June, when Queen Victoria would lay the corner stone of the Imperial Institute during the Golden Jubilee celebrations.

Gilbert, who made a point of ignoring such affairs as royal jubilees, worked away at his lozenge plot, happy in the thought that he had won his point. But he reckoned without Sullivan. When the songs and dialogue of the new libretto were read to the composer, he made a face like seven days' rainy weather and said, "No!"—firmly and unpleasantly.

When Sullivan decided to be really stubborn, he always won the argument. Gilbert laid his plot aside and looked about for another idea, all the while grumbling and fuming.

Sullivan's malady was sapping his vitality and good humor. He had no patience left for Gilbert of all people, and no desire to be tactful. As for Gilbert, he was smarting from what he considered ill-natured criticism of his creative powers. Besides, he had his own share of ill health to struggle against. He was suffering terribly from gout. He called one of his swollen feet "Labouchere," after the editor of *Truth* who had printed scathing criticisms of Gilbert's work, and the other "Clement Scott," after the critic who had repeated the remark about *Broken Hearts*.

During the summer, Gilbert always lived at his suburban home at Uxbridge. Waiting in the station one day for the train to London, he noticed a poster advertising the wares of the Tower Furniture Company. The advertisement pictured one of the men of the Tower Guard, whose duty it is to protect the treasures kept in the old fortress. In their colorful mediaeval garb, the "beef-eaters" of the Tower make a romantic crew of warders for the grim old bastion so rich in story and legend. Here was an idea! thought Gilbert. Just as the falling of a Japanese sword suggested the idea for *The Mikado,* a picture of one of the Yeomen of the Guard suggested the opera which was eventually called after them.

Gilbert sketched out the story and took it to Sullivan. Sullivan was delighted. Here at last was a story with plausible if not exactly probable situations, with real people—and no lozenges! He agreed to set it. And then he did a quixotic thing. He went off to Algiers and the south of France, and he wrote a letter. He informed both the Cartes and Gilbert that he had decided not to do another operetta, after all.

Gilbert, who had made all the concessions so far, felt that this was the last straw. He might have made allowances for Sullivan's ill health, but what seemed incredible to him was that the composer's chief objection to continuing in the field of comic opera was the success of a rival venture, *Dorothy,* which amused the London public for five hundred nights.

Gilbert in his turn wrote a letter. His was a masterpiece. He called his partner's attention to the fact that other stage shows had not closed down merely because their *Mikado* had run for two years. What if *Dorothy* was successful? Was there not room for a few comic-opera writers in England besides themselves? And then pointed out that Sullivan was England's best composer, and he, Gilbert, its best librettist. They were as much an institution as Westminster Abbey. All this might have sounded like egoistic nonsense if it had not been true. Gilbert was merely stating facts. He closed his letter with a good-humored hint on "breaking the bank" at Monte Carlo.

As Sullivan himself said, there was nobody like Gilbert. He was a writer, and a skillful one. His letter did the trick. Sullivan returned repentant to England and undertook to write the music for *The Yeomen of the Guard*.

Before he got down to cases, however, he took time to sit for his portrait, painted by Millais, to enjoy a round of social affairs, and to conduct a command performance of *The Golden Legend* at Albert Hall. Queen Victoria came up to congratulate him after the performance.

"Why don't you write a grand opera, Sir Arthur? You would do it so well!" With this simple remark the Queen did what his serious friends in the musical world had not been able to do. Sullivan was convinced that his comic-opera work was beneath him, that he should bring it to an end, and occupy himself exclusively with serious work.

Having pledged his word to collaborate on the *Yeomen,* however, he went ahead with the project. As he got into it, the story pleased him more and more. The period of Henry VIII had inspired him as early as 1877, when he had written his *Incidental Music to Henry VIII* (Shakespeare). There was nothing halfhearted about the way he threw himself into the task. Gilbert had at last given him what he wanted—romance, love interest, pathos, gentle humor. If it was not grand opera, it was at least a stepping stone leading in that direction.

The piece was produced at the Savoy Theatre on October 3rd, 1888. The famous Barrington was absent from the cast, having undertaken to become a producer in his own right. Gilbert had written a play for him, *Brantinghame Hall,* with which *The Mikado's* Pooh-Bah was tobogganing toward the bankruptcy courts. Grossmith was still with the Savoy, however, and as Jack

The Yeomen of the Guard

Point in *The Yeomen of the Guard* he was to make his name memorable for generations.

The scene on which the Savoy curtain rose was Tower Green in the sixteenth century. Imprisoned in the grim old bastion in the background is a gallant man and a brave soldier, Colonel Fairfax. His only crime lay in possessing rich lands coveted by a kinsman. The unscrupulous relative, despairing of Fairfax's death on the field of battle, bethought himself of some quick way to inherit the soldier's lands. Witchcraft provided the answer. The very thing, thought the schemer. Did not Fairfax fool around with scientific experiments? Would it not be easy to persuade super-stitious neighbors that his retorts, mortars, and pestles were the apparatus of a sorcerer? As for buying off a few judges, what could be easier? So it was done, and Fairfax was charged with having dealings with the devil. He was condemned to death.

The handsome and brave Fairfax has many friends in the Tower. Sergeant Meryll, commander of the Yeomen of the Guard, and his daughter Phoebe are stanch friends, and so is Sir Richard Cholmondeley, Lieutenant of the Tower. But none of them has the power to help Fairfax. This is a real grief to Sergeant Meryll, who has good cause to love Fairfax. The soldier once saved the old yeoman's life on the field of battle. As for Phoebe, the beautiful girl who has spent all her lonely young life in the grim Tower, she is frankly in love with the gallant Colonel.

Phoebe has brought her spinning wheel to the green, and as she works, she sings a plaintive little tune, *When maiden loves, she sits and sighs*. Poor Phoebe has cause to sigh and weep, for within a few hours the beheading block is to be set up on the green and unfortunate Fairfax is to die.

To make her day more miserable, the loutish jailer and assistant

tormentor of the Tower, Wilfred Shadbolt, intrudes on her sorrow
with declarations of his love. The very thought of the ugly brute
of a jailer makes Phoebe's flesh crawl; so she picks up her spinning
wheel and leaves him with a sharp rebuke. Wilfred, stupid and
woebegone, shuffles out after her.

With a vigorous song, the Tower Warders march onto the
green, followed by a crowd of citizens. Dame Caruthers, housekeeper of the Tower, enters in sharp argument with tearful
Phoebe. Stoutly maintaining that the prisoner deserves his fate,
the old housekeeper goes on to defend the history of the bloody
Tower:

> "The screw may twist and the rack may turn,
> And men may bleed and men may burn,
> O'er London town and its golden hoard
> I keep my silent watch and ward!"

Her song is grim, but so is the old lady who has lived all her life
within the walls of the dungeon and who admits that she loves
every stone of it.

Both Phoebe and her father are glad when Dame Caruthers
goes off with the crowd of citizens and yeomen. They discuss
the distressing predicament of their friend, and Sergeant Meryll
whispers to his daughter that there may still be hope. His son,
Phoebe's brother Leonard, is to return that very day, he tells her.
Leonard has been retired from active duty as a soldier, and given
a commission as one of the Yeomen of the Guard. It is Meryll's
idea to get his son to go away without making himself known to
the other Yeomen. A uniform will be given Fairfax who will im-
personate Leonard. When the headsman goes to the prisoner's
cell, he will find only Colonel Fairfax's discarded clothing, and

the prisoner himself will be quite safe under the very noses of his warders.

When Leonard arrives, he agrees at once to lend himself to the plan. Phoebe is overjoyed at the thought that her adored Fairfax will soon be a free man.

A babble of voices gets louder and louder. A crowd of shabby men and women pour through the wide gates to the Tower Green. Running at the head of the crowd are two poor strolling players, Jack Point and Elsie Maynard. Jack Point is in jester's garb, with cap and bells, and though he is terrified of the people who have taken it into their heads to torment the two entertainers, he turns bravely and tries to make a merry joke. He and Elsie agree to sing to the crowd. Their song *I have a song to sing, O!* has a lurking pathos in its beautiful melody, something suggestive of tragedy. A strange song for a jester, surely.

The crowd is not pleased, and begins to menace the two frightened players again, but they are saved from further abuse by the Lieutenant of the Tower. He takes a fancy to Jack Point and Elsie, and makes them a strange proposition. He tells them of the prisoner Fairfax, and says that Fairfax has a mind to cheat his treacherous kinsman by marrying before he dies. In that way, his lands will go to his wife. The Lieutenant asks Elsie if she will marry the prisoner, who is to die within an hour. His death will set her free, with more money than she ever thought to possess.

Elsie consents to the marriage, and so does Jack Point after some hesitation. The jester says ruefully:

> "Though as a general rule of life
> I don't allow my promised wife,
> My lovely bride that is to be,
> To marry anyone but me."

Unaware of the plans of Phoebe and her father to set him free, Colonel Fairfax marries Elsie, who is led into his cell blindfolded. He takes scant notice of the girl, who in one hour will be his widow—or so he and she both think. Neither would be able to recognize the other if they met face to face ten minutes later.

When the door to Fairfax's cell is opened by the Sergeant a little later, the prisoner is amazed to hear his old friend ordering him to shave his beard and put on the uniform which the Sergeant has brought—and to hurry! Fairfax obeys like a man in a daze. He can hardly believe his good fortune when he finds himself free, with everyone accepting him as the Sergeant's son. He has a moment's regret for the hasty marriage with the unknown girl, and wonders how he can rid himself of that bond; but on the whole he is glad enough just to know that the headsman's ax has been cheated.

There is a great to-do in the Tower when Fairfax's escape is discovered. Everyone searches—or pretends to search—for the prisoner. Fairfax enjoys the joke of joining the warders in the search for himself. Of course, he is not found. The only one who does not rejoice is Wilfred Shadbolt—and perhaps Dame Caruthers. Shadbolt, being the head jailer, will be held responsible for the escape.

Several others find the news alarming. Elsie bitterly regrets having married a man she does not know. Instead of being a widow according to plan, she is a wife. Jack Point realizes that there is no hope for him as long as Elsie is Fairfax's wife and Fairfax is alive.

Jack Point plots with Wilfred Shadbolt. They make up a story that the jailer saw the prisoner escaping and shot him through the head as he tried to swim to safety across the River Thames.

They tell their tale, and everyone accepts it. Only Fairfax, Phoebe, and Sergeant Meryll know the truth. Elsie, free at last as she thinks, falls in love with the supposed Leonard. Fairfax, not dreaming that Elsie is his wife, loves her in return and is vexed that he should be bound to an unknown girl. However, through a chance remark of Dame Caruthers, he discovers the truth. Overjoyed, he loses no time in telling Elsie of his love. She agrees to marry him, still thinking, of course, that he is Leonard.

Phoebe, who loves Fairfax desperately, is overwhelmed with grief. In her anguish, she makes a remark in the hearing of Wilfred Shadbolt which leads him to suspect the truth. He angrily charges Phoebe with having aided in the plot to free the prisoner. Appalled at what she has unwittingly done, Phoebe agrees to marry the repulsive jailer if he will keep silent.

Dame Caruthers eavesdrops on their conversation, and as a price of her silence she demands that Sergeant Meryll marry *her*. Just as all this has been arranged, in comes the real Leonard with a reprieve for Fairfax. There is no longer any need for Fairfax to hide. He may come to life—and he does.

When the news is brought to Elsie, she is in despair again. Married to Fairfax, she may not marry her true love, she thinks. Someone tells her that Fairfax is looking for her. As he comes from the Tower, she hides her face in her hands. Unable to look at him as she talks, she brokenly confesses her love for "Leonard," but dutifully promises to remain the wife of the man she wedded in such haste. Then Fairfax speaks, and Elsie realizes with wonder and joy that the Leonard she knew and loved is her husband. Jack Point, poor lovelorn fool, falls insensible at her feet.

Fairfax's reprieve has not altered the fact that Phoebe and her father helped a Tower prisoner to escape. They must keep their marriage promises or invite exposure, disgrace, and imprisonment. The comic opera ends on a note of frustration and sadness, and seems no more comic than poor Jack Point himself.

The Savoy audience was puzzled. Here were their beloved Gilbert and Sullivan in a new mood. The story was serious, tragic even, and this fact made the humor seem a trifle out of place. Some were of a mind not to like it at all. Writers of comic opera should stick to comedy and leave sorrow without the door, they said. Others fell under the spell of the beautiful poetry and the haunting music.

Gilbert and Sullivan had their way. *The Yeomen of the Guard* was a success. And yet—

The Mikado had had a first run of two years. *The Yeomen* did not measure up. Both Gilbert and Sullivan felt let down.

The Yeomen of the Guard is one of the hardest of all the operas to play successfully, for the very reason that its mood is hard to capture. Some casts have played it as a serious story with comic relief. Others have played it as a comedy throughout, burlesquing the serious parts until they become grotesque, even nauseating. How did Gilbert intend that it be played? Only those who saw it at the Savoy the fall of 1888 can say, and their comments are contradictory.

It is possible that Gilbert himself did not know how to reconcile the comedy and tragedy of his work. It has been said that Jack Point was Gilbert's portrait of himself. Many have found Jack Point out of place in the grim, sad story of the Tower. Perhaps *The Yeomen of the Guard* will, like its creator and poor Jack Point, be a thing of conflicting, contradictory moods forever.

Whatever the verdict on the opera as a whole, there is no doubt that there are some beautiful moments in the story and score. The opening song, sung by Phoebe alone as she sits at her spinning wheel, is pensive in mood, the music sighing with the maiden. As a spinning-wheel song, of which there are many little masterpieces, Sullivan's *When maiden loves, she sits and sighs* takes its

place with Schubert's *Gretchen* and the famous song from Flo-
tow's *Martha.*

Were I thy bride, another of Phoebe's dainty songs, is graceful,
flowing melody wedded to words both poetic and humorous. In
connection with this song, the composer once revealed how he
wrote the melodies which are so spontaneous that they seem to
have written themselves. Having read Gilbert's verses carefully,
to determine the verse pattern, he experimented with musical
rhythms. On a sheet of music staff paper, he set down various
rhythm patterns, without reference to melodic curve. With notes
all on the same line, or with a short-hand system of dots and
dashes, he worked out his problem. For *Were I thy bride* he set
down eight different rhythms which seemed possible to him,
three of them being for four-four time, two for three-four, one for
five-eight, two for six-eight, and one for two-four. The decision
between five eighth notes and a dotted quarter note in a measure,
or eight eighth notes was often the decision between the commonplace and the musically interesting. Only after he had worked
out the rhythmic pattern which seemed best did the composer
consider the melody. They were always separate matters for Sullivan—and rhythm came first.

In the autumn of our life is a four-part setting for male voices,
impressive and vigorous. The double chorus, with the crowd singing their *Tower Warders* against the simple unison passage for the
Yeomen, is most effective.

Sullivan gave Dame Caruthers' song about the Tower, *The
screw may twist and the rack may turn,* a gloomy, heavy melody.
It is preceded by a majestic orchestral prelude which is repeated
several times in the opera to suggest the idea of the Tower, a kind
of Wagnerian *leit-motif.*

Is life a boon? is good poetry joined with sensitive music. The composer gave just the right touch of gentle melancholy to the questing words.

Oh! a private buffoon is a light-hearted loon is an autobiographical song with a difference. Gilbert was surely voicing some of his own complaints in this lyric. He had learned that there are serious drawbacks to being a professional "funny man." Sullivan condoled with him and gave him some amusing chords for humorous emphasis in this clever song for Jack Point.

Light-hearted melody and rhythm are given the *Trio* sung by Elsie, Phoebe, and Fairfax. In the midst of the seriousness and gloom, there is welcome relief in *A man who would woo a fair maid.*

The *Quartet,* for Elsie, Phoebe, Fairfax, and Jack Point, is light and frivolous on the surface, but there is an undercurrent of yearning, even of pathos, as the singers tell about

> "When a wooer
> Goes a-wooing."

A downright merry song is given Jack Point and Wilfred Shadbolt for their *Duet.* Never did Sullivan's music show a nimbler pair of dancing feet than in his setting for *Hereupon we're both agreed,* where Gilbert gave him verses like:

> "And a lively one I'll be,
> Wag-a-wagging,
> Never flagging!"

There is infectious gayety in this "tale of cock and bull" told by the two ill-assorted clowns of the play.

But, of course, the real gem of the opera is the duet for Elsie and

Jack Point, *I have a song to sing, O*. Its swinging rhythm suggests dancing feet and carnival, but the words themselves and the melody are anything but light-hearted. The combination of gay dance rhythm with a plaintive air is inexpressibly charming.

The orchestral accompaniment with its drone bass conjures up a picture of barrel organs—playing in the rain or fog, perhaps, with not too many customers in the streets. If ever music suggested the tawdry, pathetic life of street entertainers, this music does. It makes one wonder if there might be a grain of truth in the story which has persisted through the years, that Sullivan's mother as a child sang for pennies in the streets of London.

From the first provocative *I have a song to sing,* O, to the last

> "Heighdy! Heighdy!
> Misery me, lackadaydee!
> His pains were o'er, and he sighed no more,
> For he lived in the love of a ladye,"

the song is a perfect setting for a perfect poem.

This is the one song for which Gilbert suggested the music. Sullivan had difficulty with the setting, and appealed to the librettist for help. "I know you often have some tune in mind when you write the songs," he said to Gilbert. "Hum this one for me."

Gilbert confessed that a Cornish carol, sung by the sailors on his yacht in the dog-watch, had suggested the pattern of *I have a song to sing, O*. He began to hum the carol. After a few bars, Sullivan held up his hand. "Stop! No more! I have it!"

Gilbert always maintained that it was his humming out of tune that made the composer stop him so quickly. The truth of the matter, of course, was that Sullivan merely wanted the rhythm pattern, not the actual melody.

Phoebe of *The Yeomen of the Guard* is undoubtedly the most human of all Gilbert's heroines. For that reason, we cannot bear to think of this lovely girl married to the ugly Shadbolt. Perhaps that is why her first song seems poignantly sad, in retrospect. Whatever the reason, Phoebe's spinning-wheel song has the wistful quality which colors even the humorous passages of this strange comic opera.

When maid-en loves, she sits and sighs, She wan-ders to and fro; Un-bid-den tear-drops

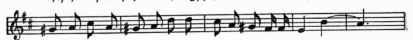

Fill her eyes, And to all ques-tions she re-plies With a sad "heigh - ho !"

Ev-'ry sound be-comes a song, All is right and noth-ing's wrong!

12

NOTHING could persuade him to write another opera with Gilbert, Sullivan decided. At first, he put his librettist off with the old excuse, that he was tired of writing music for unreal situations. Gilbert, who had just given the composer a true-to-life story in *The Yeoman of the* Guard, said frankly that Sullivan was unfair. Finally the composer gave his real reason. He wanted to write the serious opera which he and Carte had been planning for a long time past.

It was Carte's idea to produce all-English grand opera. He wanted to build an opera house dedicated to such works. And Sullivan should write the first one.

Gilbert was more than surprised when Sullivan asked him to write the libretto. The composer probably knew that Gilbert would not accept the proposition, or he would not have made it. Gilbert told both Carte and Sullivan that he did not believe that an English grand opera would succeed. He himself did not care to be associated with a failure. And that was that.

However, Gilbert *did* want to be associated with another successful comic opera. He had a large house to keep up, expensive entertaining to do, and costly yachts to man and keep in repair. He had to make money! He was infuriated when Sullivan calmly went off to Monte Carlo with the Prince of Wales and wrote that he had no intention of playing second fiddle in the future as he had been doing for twelve years past.

Differences of opinion grew rapidly into a quarrel, with Sullivan writing his true thoughts to Carte, and Carte forwarding the letters to Gilbert. Sullivan's letters were ill-natured in the extreme. He gave vent to all his long-pent-up dislike of Gilbert's bullying methods at the theater, of his rudeness to those who made suggestions, of his tiring the actors so that they could not sing, of ruining musical effects in order to make the words more prominent.

Gilbert raged and wrote letters, the kind of letters that got results. He brought Sullivan to his senses. After all, the composer needed money, too. His serious music brought him glory, but the comic operas brought him gold. Sullivan came back to London, where he met Gilbert, shook hands, and agreed to bury the hatchet. A month later, Gilbert called on the composer with the story of *The Gondoliers*.

After the rain, the rainbow! Not one line of poetry, not one measure of music in *The Gondoliers* gives any indication of the friction between the two men.

It took Gilbert five months to write the libretto. It was sent piece by piece to Sullivan, who was more and more delighted with every song that arrived by post. Gilbert was working at Uxbridge, Sullivan at Grove House in Weybridge. Each in his own way was enjoying the quiet beauty of a country retreat, and each in his own way was busy creating beauty.

During the quarrel which preceded *The Gondoliers*, Gilbert had written one very sensible paragraph. In answer to the accusation that the composer had been taking second place for twelve years, the playwright said, in effect, that if this was so, then Sullivan had only himself to blame. If Sullivan was hinting that Gilbert should henceforth take second place, he might as well understand right off that this could not be. Henceforth we must meet as master and master, said Gilbert with dignity and finality. And as master and master they met, in the gayest, most tuneful, wittiest, most humorous of all the operas, not even excepting the splendid *Mikado*.

Both Gilbert and Sullivan caught the spirit of sunny, songloving Italy in *The Gondoliers,* which opens in Venice. Charming young girls in colorful peasant costumes have brought roses to the Piazzetta, where they wait for the gondola of the brothers Marco and Giuseppe Palmieri, the handsomest young gondoliers in all Venice. When the boys arrive, they are loaded down with flowers and surrounded by laughing girls the minute they step from their boat. The opening chorus of girls, with Marco and Giuseppe answering gallantly, is light-hearted and fresh as spring itself.

The *Duet* of the gondoliers is a song born of the languorous sunny south. Gilbert's lyrics are charming. Sullivan's music catches their spirit, which is the Latin spirit of romance and sultry beauty. The partners wrote few songs as lovely as the one with the lines:

> "When morning is breaking,
> Our couches forsaking,
> To greet their awaking
>   With carols we come;
> At summer day's nooning,
> When weary lagooning,
> Our mandolins tuning,
>   We lazily thrum."

The Gondoliers

Marco and Giuseppe have come to choose brides from among the pretty girls, and—though we take this with a grain of salt—they say that they have no preferences and so will make their choice in a game of blind man's buff. There is much merry laughter, and short skirts flirt provocatively during the game. In spite of blindfolds, Marco and Giuseppe manage to catch the prettiest girls of the group—Tessa and Gianetta. Marco and Gianetta dance off together. Giuseppe and Tessa join them. The rest of the girls follow to attend the weddings.

When the laughing crowd is gone, another gondola arrives. A strange group steps out. The Duke of Plaza-Toro, the Duchess, their daughter Casilda, and their attendant Luiz, with drum. All are dressed in fine but faded clothes. It is pretty clear that the ducal fortune is not what it was.

Each member of the party introduces himself or herself with a delightful song begun by the Duke with the lines:

> "From the sunny Spanish shore,
> The Duke of Plaza-Tor!"

All join in the rapid

> "If ever, ever, ever
> They get back to Spain,
> They will never, never, never
> Cross the sea again!"

The shabby little party makes its way to the door of the ducal palace of the Grand Inquisitor. While they are waiting for someone to answer the door, the Duke tells Casilda that he has a wonderful surprise for her. It seems that when their daughter was six months old, the Duke and Duchess arranged a marriage between her and the infant son of the King of Barataria. The Duke explains further:

"Shortly after the ceremony, that misguided monarch abandoned the creed of his forefathers, and became a Wesleyan Methodist of the most bigoted and persecuting type. The Grand Inquisitor, determined that the innovation should not be perpetuated in Barataria, caused your smiling and unconscious husband to be stolen and conveyed to Venice. A fortnight since, the Methodist monarch and all his Wesleyan Court were killed in an insurrection, and we are here to ascertain the whereabouts of your husband, and to hail you, our daughter, as Her Majesty, the reigning Queen of Barataria!"

After making this speech to his astounded daughter, the Duke breaks into song, the delightful autobiographical ballad *In enterprise of martial kind*. He and his Duchess then enter the Palace. Casilda promptly behaves in a manner very odd for a young Queen in search of her King. She rushes into the arms of the drummer Luiz. They sing a woeful duet about

"There was a time—
A time for ever gone—ah, woe is me!"

in which they accept the fate which is tearing them one from the other.

The Duke and Duchess come from the Palace with the Grand Inquisitor, Don Alhambra del Bolero, who has startling news for them. His song *I stole the Prince and brought him here* is a wonderful blending of Gilbert's and Sullivan's genius. The words are so musical that they seem to sing even without music, and the music is so light-hearted that it seems to laugh and chuckle even without the humor of the words.

In this song, Don Alhambra explains that when he stole the royal babe, he gave him into the keeping of a "highly respectable gondolier," to rear "with his own beloved brattling." The boys were of the same age, and somehow, as time went on, the gondolier forgot which one was his, which was the Prince. One thing is sure, however, the Inquisitor explains to Casilda, either Marco or Giuseppe Palmieri is the "royal babe":

> "Well, one of the two (who will soon be here)—
> But *which* of the two is not quite clear—
> Is the Royal Prince you married!
>
> Search in and out and round about,
>   And you'll discover never
>   A tale so free from every doubt—
> All probable, possible shadow of doubt—
> All possible doubt whatever!"

The *Quintet* which follows, sung by the Duke, the Duchess, Casilda, Luiz, and the Grand Inquisitor, is the jolliest, most devil-may-care tune for words that skip and dance like children at play:

> "String the lyre and fill the cup,
>   Lest on sorrow we should sup.
> Hop and skip to Fancy's fiddle,
> Hands across and down the middle—
> Life's perhaps the only riddle
>   That we shrink from giving up!"

When the Duke and his family go into the Palace, the happy gondoliers and their brides and the girls come dancing in. Tessa sings a tender little song, which has just the right amount of happiness and lingering regret for a young bride:

> "When a merry maiden marries,
>   Sorrow goes, and pleasure tarries;
>   Every sound becomes a song,
>   All is right, and nothing's wrong!"

The Duke's party and Don Alhambra break in upon this merry scene. What was all happiness and laughter turns to dismay when the two bridegrooms are told that one of them is a King. The Inquisitor declares that both must go to Barataria and rule jointly until it can be determined which one is the true King. He sternly forbids them to take their wives, however, a decree which is not at all to the liking of the newlyweds. Don Alhambra comforts them by saying that the separation will be brief. An old nurse, who knows which one is the King, will be brought to Barataria to solve the riddle.

The girls finally give in. Neither they nor their husbands know, of course, that the one who is King is married to Casilda. Tessa and Gianetta imagine that one of them will be Queen. They sing a saucy song with their husbands which ends:

> "Oh, 'tis a glorious thing, I ween,
>   To be a regular Royal Queen!
>   No half-and-half affair, I mean,
>   But a right-down regular Royal Queen!"

As for Marco and Giuseppe, they are inclined to undertake the job principally because it will give them a chance to introduce republican reforms. Their song in which they declare, "They all shall equal be!" is great fun.

The girls bid their husbands tearful farewells, adding a warning that they must not look at other girls:

> "And O my darling, O my pet,
> Whatever else you may forget
> In yonder isle beyond the sea,
> Do not forget you've married me!"

Act Two opens with a magnificent court scene. Marco and Giuseppe, dressed in rich regal robes, are seated on twin thrones. There is some very funny dialogue concerning the "monarchy that's tempered with Republican equality," and then Giuseppe sings the song which stands out as the cleverest of the opera— *Rising early in the morning*. It is said that Queen Victoria was very much amused at the lines:

> "Oh, philosophers may sing
> Of the troubles of a King;
> Yet the duties are delightful and the privileges great;
> But the privilege and pleasure
> That we treasure beyond measure
> Is to run on little errands for the Ministers of State."

Marco and Giuseppe are lonesome for their wives. Marco sings a charming song with just the right touch of light romance, *Take a pair of sparkling eyes*. He has barely finished when in rush the wives and the girls from Venice, singing excitedly:

> "So here we are, at the risk of our lives,
> From ever so far, and we've brought your wives—
> And to that end we've crossed the main,
> And don't intend to return again!"

The Kings are so pleased that they order a banquet and ball. The happy girls burst into song, the spirited *Dance a cachucha, fandango, bolero.*

Don Alhambra, coming upon this merry scene, is surprised and not too approving. He cannot agree that it is a good thing for kings to dance with their subjects, not to say their servants, as the Republican Monarchs are doing. He proceeds to tell a story with a moral—in song:

> "There lived a King, as I've been told,
> In the wonder-working days of old,
> When hearts were twice as good as gold,
>   And twenty times as mellow."

This king had republican ideas, too, it seems. He wanted everyone to be as rich as he. This, at least, was playwright Gilbert's idea of republicanism. He promoted everybody "to the top of the tree," so that Lord Chancellors, Bishops, Ambassadors, Prime Ministers, Dukes, Field Marshals, and Admirals "grow like asparagus in May." The result of all this nonsense was that:

> "That King, although no one denies
> His heart was of abnormal size,
> Yet he'd have acted otherwise
>   If he had been acuter.
> The end is easily foretold:
> When every blessed thing you hold
> Is made of silver, or of gold,
>   You long for simple pewter.
> When you have nothing else to wear
> But cloth of gold and satins rare,
> For cloth of gold you cease to care—
>   Up goes the price of shoddy.

"In short, whoever you may be,
To this conclusion you'll agree,
When everyone is somebodee,
Then no one's anybody!"

Verse like this makes one wish that Gilbert had been "acuter,"
politically speaking. He was so clever that he might have laughed
to scorn some very real abuses in his day. As it was, he lashed out
at everything, until, as one critic said, he was suspected of being
an anarchist disguised as a Tory.

Don Alhambra proceeds to spill the beans about Casilda. The
wives, listening in, are properly indignant. The *Quartet,* in which
Marco, Giuseppe, Gianetta, and Tessa say that the entangled
situation must be straightened out "in contemplative fashion,"
is one of the most amusing songs of the opera.

Announced by pompous music, the Duke of Plaza-Toro and
his Duchess enter. They are splendidly dressed, as become members of a Court. Astonished at the informality of the dancing he
has witnessed, the Duke decides to show the two kings how they
should dance. Sullivan wrote gavotte music for the amusing scene
in which Marco and Giuseppe try to dance in courtly style. Watching their efforts critically, the Duke first says:

"That's, if anything, *too* unbending—
Too aggressively stiff and grand."

Then, as they modify their haughty demeanor, he remarks:

"Now to the other extreme you're tending—
Don't be so deucedly condescending!"

The old nurse finally arrives. She points out the true King of
Barataria. It is Luiz! Luiz, the drummer! Casilda and Luiz rush

joyously into each other's arms. As for the gondoliers and their
brides, they are happy enough to have each other, and waste no
regrets on their throne for a day. The opera ends on a gladsome
note with the tune of the cachucha:

Say, why is ev-'ry-thing   Ei - ther at six-es or at sev-ens?

13

HE PUBLIC'S whole-hearted acceptance of *The Gondoliers* cheered Gilbert so that he wrote a gracious letter to Sullivan, giving him generous credit for his part in the success. Having his libretto set to such beautiful music, said Gilbert, "gives one the chance of shining right through the twentieth century with a reflected light."

Sullivan replied in kind: "Don't talk of reflected light. In such a perfect book as *The Gondoliers* you shine with an individual brilliancy which no other writer can hope to attain."

The atmosphere had never been more serene. Both artists were determined to maintain a cordial relationship. And then Carte bought a carpet.

It was an expensive and beautiful carpet, designed for his private office at the Savoy Theatre. The trouble was that he charged its cost against the current opera. Ordinarily nothing would have been thought of this arrangement. Carte's contract with Gilbert and Sullivan provided a set amount for the rent and upkeep of the theater, and specified equal sharing of production expenses.

However, a new factor had entered the equation with the

Queen's remark about a grand opera. Victoria's encouragement, added to the clamor of Sullivan's musical friends that he should write a work "more worthy of his genius," strengthened the composer's resolve to lay aside comic opera for grand opera. Carte wanted to share in the glory of such a venture. He was going forward with plans to build a magnificent opera house, where only English grand opera would be produced. It was understood that Sullivan was to write the opera which would ring up the curtain on English national opera. All these ambitious plans were being laid in the office with the carpet.

Gilbert objected. He said the carpet was too expensive, that it was not properly part of production costs. He felt strongly that the office which it decorated was being used more to further the grand-opera plans than to promote the Savoy comic operas. He objected to sharing the expense of a rival venture.

Gilbert had a good deal of justice on his side of the argument, but he made the mistake of losing his temper and using some ugly language when he and Carte talked the matter over. He and Carte almost came to blows. Carte followed up the quarrel with a sharp letter, in which he said that if Gilbert did not modify his conduct and speech in future, the Savoy partnership might have to be dissolved. Carte and Sullivan, the manager said cuttingly, could do without Gilbert very well.

That remark was more than Gilbert could bear. He knew that the success of the Savoy operas was due in large measure to his careful directing. He knew as well as Sullivan that as a librettist he was the best in the field. To have Carte hint that he might be brushed aside infuriated him. He wrote Sullivan demanding that he participate in a conference in Carte's office, to clear up the disputed matter of the carpet.

Sullivan arrived, not feeling very well, unhappy that the good will which had prevailed for months past should be destroyed by a carpet. Gilbert, overwrought, demanded that his collaborator take a stand on the deal, demanded, in fact, that Sullivan oppose Carte. What Gilbert did not take into consideration was the fact that Sullivan and Carte were partners, in a sense, in a new venture —the projected grand opera. The composer was in no mind to jeopardize that important work merely to satisfy Gilbert, with whose tirades he was fed up, anyway. He did what Gilbert should have known he would do—he sided with Carte.

Gilbert fumed out of the office, calling back unpleasant threats over his shoulder. He took the case to court, demanding an auditing of Carte's accounts. The public got the idea that one of the Savoy partners was charging the other two with fraud, and was shocked. The masters of mirth and melody were losing some of their glamour.

Sullivan sided with Carte, but the English courts upheld Gilbert. Having won his point in court, which was all he wanted, the victor marched straight to the vanquished, admitted that his gout had been the cause of most of the trouble, agreed to a compromise of the carpet issue, and apologized to both Carte and Sullivan for his ungentlemanly behavior and abusive language. That was Gilbert.

During all this unpleasantness, Sullivan was writing his opera. Oddly enough, Gilbert had suggested the librettist for this work, J. Sturgis, who adapted Sir Walter Scott's novel *Ivanhoe*. The composer began working on the score on May 17th, 1890, while he was staying in Weybridge. He set down a few pages, and then gave it up until June. The carpet quarrel was raging. Poor Sullivan found it hard to occupy himself with the troubles, adventures and romances of Ivanhoe, Rowena, Rebecca, and the Black Knight when disquieting letters came with every post. By September, very little of the music was written.

The composer had never been so highly strung during the writing of a score. Dissatisfied with what he had done with the first act, he put it away and began in another place, setting the duet for Rebecca and the Templar in Act Two. Before he had completed the second act, he put it with the first and started the third. He was working nervously and erratically, all the while obsessed by fears that the work would be unworthy. On December 13th, he wrote in his diary: "Put the last note to score at 6 p.m. *Absolutely finished*. Thank God. Seven months' hard labour. 715 pages of score."

The opera went into rehearsal at the elaborate theater which Carte had built and called the Royal English Opera House, on January 31st, 1891. No expense was spared. A double cast was hired to provide against such emergencies as sickness, accident, or other mishap. The sets for the three acts and nine scenes were superb and costly, and the costumes were designed by high-salaried artists and made of richest materials.

The ailing composer had truly given of his life's blood to make this opera great. When people came from all over the British Isles to attend the opening and cheered *Ivanhoe* and its composer with an abandon not customary with English audiences, Sullivan felt that he was repaid for his work and worry. This *première* was the climax of his career. Nothing would ever give him such pleasure again.

Though Gilbert was extended an invitation to attend this first performance of *Ivanhoe,* he declined churlishly. Sullivan was more hurt than he cared to admit when he read his collaborator's curt,

"I decline your stalls!" Some weeks later, Gilbert bought tickets to the opera. He even wrote Sullivan a note, in which he said that *Ivanhoe* was the first grand opera he had ever enjoyed. That was Gilbert.

The critics were generous in their praise of Sullivan's opera. The Queen wrote to congratulate him, and to thank him for dedicating the work to her. Letters of praise poured in from the musically great of the world. But—

The public came to see *Ivanhoe* for only one hundred sixty performances. Gilbert, who had never been optimistic about a long run, sat in his study and grinned like a Cheshire cat. Sullivan was miserable over the dwindling houses. He had expected a success like the two-year run of *The Mikado*. What he did not realize was that compared to the runs of other grand operas in England, *Ivanhoe* was a tremendous success. All that he could think of was that Gilbert had the right to say, "I told you so!"

Meanwhile, Gilbert had written with Alfred Cellier another comic opera, produced at the Lyric Theatre on January 4th, 1892. This was the highly successful *The Mountebanks,* based, ironically enough, on the lozenge plot which Sullivan had stubbornly refused to set.

Carte, disappointed, too, with the grand-opera venture, backed Sullivan and Sydney Grundy in a comic opera for the Savoy, *Haddon Hall.* It opened on September 24th, 1892, and closed promptly. Carte and Sullivan looked at each other in dismay. During the carpet quarrel, they had been willing to rid themselves of Gilbert forever. After *Haddon Hall,* they realized how much they needed him. Carte had to eat crow, and go to Gilbert to ask for another libretto. Gilbert, who liked nothing so much as to win

a good fight, was having the time of his life. He agreed to do
another opera with Sullivan.

The composer was vacationing on the Riviera the winter of
1893. At the end of January, Gilbert visited him for three days.
Walking along the beach near Sullivan's hotel, smoking good
cigars after an excellent dinner, breakfasting outdoors in the warm
sunshine, the two men felt that they had succeeded in wiping out
all traces of past bitterness. In the friendliest possible way, they
discussed Gilbert's new story.

The playwright went back to England to finish the libretto. In
due course of time, Sullivan tore himself away from his pleasures
and returned to England, too. He took a cottage in the country for
the summer, and began to compose. The new Savoy opera was
called *Utopia, Limited; or, The Flowers of Progress.* It was a satire
on English prudery, English polite conversation, English com-
pany-promoting, the English party system, the War Office, the
Admiralty, the Cabinet, and the sanitary laws.

The opera was ready for production in the fall. Carte gave it
a splendid mounting. Costumes and sets cost more than seven
thousand pounds. The cast, as usual, was composed of good actors
with good voices. It included two newcomers to Gilbert and
Sullivan opera—Walter Passmore, who was Grossmith's brilliant
successor, and Nancy McIntosh, an American girl, who became
famous overnight in her soprano rôle of Princess Zara. This charming young singer, an amateur who played her first part on the
stage with the aplomb of a veteran actress, so captivated Gilbert
and his wife that they adopted her legally.

Sullivan wrote some good music for *Utopia, Limited;* nevertheless, this opera is remembered for the libretto rather than the score.
Gilbert triumphed in *Utopia,* where "the play's the thing." The

book is one of his wittiest. The music critic writing for *The World*
was in the first-night audience. This was George Bernard Shaw,
who pronounced the opera the best of the Savoy series.

Of plot there is very little in the opera. The main idea is the
bringing over to the idyllic island of Utopia half a dozen important Englishman, whose instructions are to Anglicize the
people and institutions of King Paramount's dominion. The
idea originated in the brain of King Paramount's oldest daughter,
Zara, who has spent five years in England, studying the laws and
customs of the "greatest, the most powerful, the wisest country in
the world."

The Englishmen are very successful in their mission, with the
result that the days are pretty "lank and long" in Utopia. As in
England itself, "all goes right and nothing goes wrong." The
sanitary laws have been made so strict that there is no disease, and
the medical profession is dying out. The lawyers are starving, since
ideal social and legal conditions have abolished crime. The jails
have been made into apartments for working people.

King Paramount and his Court find this "dull prosperity" not
at all to their liking. Zara finds the solution. The English party
system. She explains:

"Government by Party! Introduce that great and glorious
element—at once the bulwark and foundation of England's greatness—and all will be well! No political measures will endure, because one Party will assuredly undo all that the other Party has
done; and while grouse is to be shot and foxes are to be worried
to death, the legislative action of the country will be at a standstill.
Then there will be sickness in plenty, endless lawsuits, crowded
jails, interminable confusion in the Army and Navy, and in short,
general and unexampled prosperity!"

This final English touch brings perfection to Utopia, and everyone sings happily as the last curtain falls.

On this slender plot-thread, Gilbert hung some amusing speeches, scenes, and songs. His duet for the two younger daughters of King Paramount, who have been reared by an English governess, is highly diverting. Sullivan caught his mood, and gave this prim ballad delightfully droll music. The coy young girls singing *Although of native maids the cream* furnish one of the most entertaining moments of the opera.

One of the most laughter-provoking scenes is that in which the Utopian Cabinet members are instructed how an English Cabinet Council sits. They are told to arrange their chairs in a line, with the King in the middle chair. The Christy Minstrels from America had taken London by storm. The Savoy audience was quick to see that the chair arrangement was a copy of the style of the Christy Minstrels, complete with end men and interlocutor.

Critic Shaw was particularly pleased with this scene and Sullivan's delightful music for it. Shaw wrote: "I confidently recommend those who go into solemn academic raptures over themes 'in diminution' to go and hear how prettily the chorus of the Christy Minstrels song (borrowed from the plantation song, 'Johnnie, get a gun') is used very much in diminution to make an exquisite mock banjo accompaniment." Shaw added, citing examples from the score: "We are on the plane not of bones and tambourines, but of Mozart's accompaniments to 'Scave sia il vento' in *Cosi fan tutti* and the entry of the gardener in *Le Nozze di Figaro*."

This opera contains Gilbert's famous description of the typical English girl. Though there is humor in this song, the playwright was mainly in earnest when he wrote the lines:

"Rich in the things contentment brings,
  In every pure enjoyment wealthy,
Blithe as a beautiful bird she sings,
  For body and mind are hale and healthy.
Her eyes they thrill with right goodwill—
  Her heart is light as a floating feather—
As pure and bright as the mountain rill
  That leaps and laughs in the Highland heather!

  Go search the world and search the sea,
  Then come you home and sing with me
  There's no such gold and no such pearl
  As a bright and beautiful English girl!"

Sullivan wrote a joyous tune for this song, and a roguish melody
for the *Quartet* which follows. When the unnaturally stiff little
Princesses discover that they have been on the wrong track with
their blushing and their downcast eyes, they join in singing the
sparkling:

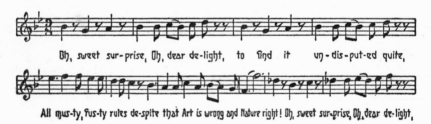

Oh, sweet sur-prise, Oh, dear de-light, to find it un-dis-put-ed quite,
All mus-ty, fus-ty rules de-spite that Art is wrong and Nature right! Oh, sweet sur-prise, Oh, dear de-light,

Despite all the favorable criticisms of this truly clever opera,
Utopia, Limited enjoyed only moderate success. Within three
months the ticket sales were falling off to such an extent that
Carte wrote the partners in reference to their next opera: "There

is no doubt in my mind that what the people want now is simply 'fun' and little else . . ."

No talk of a "next opera" went on between Gilbert and Sullivan for some time, however. Sullivan and Burnand revived their early comic opera *The Contrabandista,* gave it some new tunes and dialogue, and Carte produced it at the Savoy as *The Chieftain.* It was a dismal failure. Sullivan returned to more serious music with his incidental score for *King Arthur,* produced at the Lyceum. It was not until the end of 1895 that Gilbert completed a new libretto, which he called *The Grand Duke; or, The Statutory Duel.* Sullivan went right to work on the music.

On March 7th, 1896, the last of the Gilbert and Sullivan operas was staged at the Savoy. Because their old fans were hoping for another *Pinafore* or *Mikado* from the beloved team, they turned out in force for the first night, and cheered loyally. But a brilliant first night does not ensure the success of a work, and loyalty to friends does not hide their weaknesses from the world.

All too soon, London discovered that Gilbert's last libretto was as poor a piece of mumbo-jumbo as had been foisted off on the public for many years. If the magic name of *Gilbert* had not been attached, no manager would have looked twice at the script. An uninspired book brought forth only uninspired music, for the most part, and Sullivan came in for his share of adverse criticism.

The Grand Duke marked the end of the greatest collaboration in theatrical history. The composer blamed the librettist, the librettist blamed the composer. Gilbert and Sullivan never spoke to each other again after this opera, the only true failure in the series.

The less said of *The Grand Duke* the better. The playwright showed himself tired and empty of ideas throughout. The story itself was adapted from a printed source, a tale called *The Duke's Surprise*, which had even been used before in comic opera—*The Prima Donna*, by H. B. Farnie and Tito Mattei, produced in 1889.

The plot is so involved and absurd, and the characters so unreal, that it is difficult to make head or tail of the doings of the Grand Duke Rudolph and the actors and actresses of Ernest Dummkopf's company, who are the principals in the piece. It is impossible to figure out what Gilbert was trying to satirize, if, indeed, he himself knew. He has a nasty jibe or two at theatrical managers. Did he have Carte in mind? He says some sharp things about actors and actresses, and comes close to his old form with

> "Oh, the man who can drive a theatrical team,
> With wheelers and leaders in order supreme,
> Can govern and rule, with a wave of his fin,
> All Europe—with Ireland thrown in!"

He makes mockery of political plotters, with his hocus-pocus about sausage rolls, the eating of which identifies the revolutionists to each other. He makes mockery, too, of romance and love. He is a cynical old man, sneering:

> "Here they come, the couple plighted—
> On life's journey gaily start them.
> Soon to be for aye united,
> Till divorce or death shall part them."

He jeers at stinginess, representing the Duke and Duchess-to-be as Scrooges of the most fantastic type. The Duke's betrothed speaks thus:

"I often picture us in the long, cold, dark December evenings, sitting close to each other and singing impassioned duets to keep us warm, and thinking of all the lovely things we could afford to buy if we chose, and, at the same time, planning out our lives in a spirit of the most rigid and exacting economy!"

But even as he touches each subject, Gilbert lets it go and veers off to something else. Like a sailing ship in light, variable winds, he tacks crazily and seems to get nowhere.

In the songs, he went back to some of the older ones and copied them badly. Julia's ballad *How would I play this part* is Phoebe's *Were I thy bride* with its beauty dimmed and its freshness gone. Rudolph's song *When you find you're a broken-down critter* is a pale carbon of *Iolanthe's* Lord Chancellor's nightmare.

Only two numbers in the whole operetta are worth remarking— the quintet *Strange views some people hold!* and the opening chorus in Act Two, *As before you we defile.* For this chorus, Sullivan wrote dignified music worthy to be placed beside his Greek dance in *Patience:*

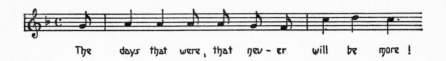

The days that were, that nev-er will be more !

14

HAT a good thing it would have been for his art had Sullivan given up his social life, which demanded too much of his ailing body. It would have been a good thing for his health if he could have given up both. As it was, he burned the candle at both ends. Traveling, gambling, horse racing, entertaining royalty—these occupied him more and more. And between social engagements, he composed feverishly. He was obsessed with the fear that his muse might desert him.

He toyed with several ideas after *The Grand Duke.* He would write another grand opera, based on the King Arthur legend. He would compose an operetta for the singer Yvette Gilbert. He wound up by agreeing to write a ballet for Queen Victoria's Diamond Jubilee, to be produced in the spring of 1897. Then, at the end of the summer of 1896, he went to the Engadine in Switzerland. He stayed a short time, and pushed on restlessly to Munich and Vienna. He looked in vain for some of the old cafés in the cobble-paved streets which he and George Grove had explored years before when they looked for Schubert's *Rosamunde.*

The Englishwoman Empress Frederick of Germany invited

him to visit her. He promptly went to Friedrichoł, where he cheered a lonely woman in a foreign land, and an old Emperor dying of cancer. Depressed more than ever, the composer made his way back to London, only to find the city choked with fog. Back to the Continent he went, renting a villa at Beaulieu, near Monte Carlo.

During January, 1897, he worked on the ballet, which was called *Victoria and Merrie England*. It was an intensely national work, in which Sullivan sketched the history of English music down through the centuries. It was performed in May and was acknowledged to be the most attractive piece performed in the Jubilee year. The composer was rewarded by an invitation to Windsor and the Jubilee Medal.

Because it was the thing to do, he went to Beyreuth in August, 1897, to attend the Wagner Festival. He did not change his opinion of Wagner. He wrote in his diary: "What a curious mixture of sublimity and absolute puerile drivel are all these Wagner operas! Sometimes the story and action would disgrace even a Surrey pantomime." The Surrey Theatre to which he referred was, at this time, the home of crude melodrama.

He was home again by fall. In November he went to hear Coleridge-Taylor's *Hiawatha*. Sullivan instantly recognized the young composer's genius, and did all he could to make London aware of it. Of *Hiawatha,* and its composer, he said:

"The music is fresh and original—he has melody and harmony in abundance, and his scoring is brilliant and full of colour—at times luscious, rich and sensual."

However he may have tried to deceive himself, Sullivan was itching to write another comic opera. Librettist Gilbert was lost to him; so he turned to other writers. Comyns Carr and Arthur

Pinero proposed to write a libretto together. Carr read the scenario to Sullivan, who decided to set it, even though he was afraid it might be too serious. How Gilbert would have laughed at his serious-minded composer, had he known!

The work gave Sullivan so much trouble that he often felt like giving it up. It was not a true opera, but rather a play with descriptive music. Sullivan struggled mightily with Pinero's flowery diction, and when his music was written, he disliked it. This play, *The Beauty Stone,* was produced at the end of May, 1898. It lasted seven weeks.

In October he conducted the Leeds Festival music for the last time. He had not missed a festival since 1878. An audience which had known him for twenty years greeted him with a tremendous ovation. He wrote in his diary:

"After the last performance, the Chorus cheered me so tremendously, that I suddenly broke down, and ran off . . . crying like a child."

It was as if both Sullivan and his friends of Leeds had a premonition that this would be their last meeting.

On the twenty-first anniversary of *The Sorcerer,* which had been produced first in November, 1877, Carte offered a gala performance to the London public. The house was filled to overflowing with faithful Savoyards, who insisted that composer and librettist should come before the curtain for a bow. The partners came out to acknowledge the friendly reception of their work, but they came from opposite sides of the stage and neither looked at nor spoke to the other.

Shortly after this unhappy episode, Sullivan met Basil Hood, a talented young dramatist who wanted to write a light opera with him. He had a story with an Eastern atmosphere, entitled *Hassan.*

The composer was favorably impressed and determined to write the music. However, he could not get down to it, no matter how he tried. He found himself making all sorts of excuses. An attack of influenza sent him scurrying to the warm Riviera. From there he went to Switzerland, where Hood joined him. Work on the opera progressed, but slowly. Finally, Sullivan decided that the Swiss surroundings were not suitable for the "Persian opera." He returned to England, and finished the music in the house he had taken at Wokingham.

Retitled *The Rose of Persia,* the opera was produced on November 29th, 1899, at the Savoy. It was a success. How much Sullivan needed that success to buoy up his spirits is indicated by the entry in his diary on the opening night:

"I conducted as usual. Hideously nervous as usual—great reception as usual—great house as usual—excellent performance as usual—everything as usual—except that the piece is really a great success, I think, which is *unusual* lately."

After *The Rose of Persia,* the composer was disturbed and aimless. His illness not only sapped his strength of body but also rendered him dull mentally. The Boer War was on, and the composer set Kipling's *The Absent-minded Beggar* to music, producing a song which stirred the nation much as the older "We don't want to fight, but, by jingo, if we do—" had. It was a rabble-rouser. People sang it in the streets, troops marched to the ships singing it, and dollars dropped into the rich chest of the War Charity to the tune of "Pay! Pay! Pay!"

Basil Hood brought Sullivan another good libretto, *The Emerald Isle.* The composer found it very good, and undertook the music. But he would take up his pen only to lay it down again. He was increasingly restless. He traveled back and forth

across the Channel, between London and Paris and Monte Carlo.
He wrote letters and sent telegrams every day to Mrs. Ronalds,
even if he had seen her a few hours before. His need for human
companionship grew. More and more he dreaded the lonely hours
of composing.

When *Patience* was revived in a splendid performance at the
Savoy, Sullivan for the first time could not summon strength to
conduct the first night. Carte and Gilbert took the bows, and
Sullivan lay in bed, lonely and in pain.

Gilbert became ill shortly afterward. He was too crippled with
rheumatic fever to come to see his old partner when news reached
him of Sullivan's serious condition, but he wrote a warm, friendly
letter to the sick man. The partners were friends again.

Late in the afternoon of November 21st, Sullivan seemed to feel
better than he had since the first day of his sickness. No one was
prepared for his sudden passing at six the next morning. Before
the royal physician, Sir Thomas Barlow, could reach him, he was
gone. Mrs. Ronalds made frantic efforts to come to him, but she,
also, was too late.

Queen Victoria arranged for the first part of the funeral service
to be held at the Chapel Royal, where Sullivan himself in the
days of his choristership had often sung the sad last service. From
the Chapel the funeral procession passed to St. Paul's, where the
composer was buried in the crypt. There the Savoy chorus sang,
as best they could, the beautiful *Brother, thou art gone before
us.*

The funeral procession on its way to St. Paul's Cathedral went
by way of the Embankment, where Carte lay very ill in his house
in Adelphi Terrace. Though his doctor and nurses had been careful to keep the news of Sullivan's death from him, he must have

discovered the truth for himself. Pulling himself up to his bed-room window, he watched the cortège.

"I have just seen the last of my old friend Sullivan," he said brokenly as he was led back to his bed. A few months later, Carte, too, was dead.

Some years later, when a memorial to Sullivan was to be placed in Savoy Gardens, it was Gilbert who suggested the appropriate quotation from the Savoy operas:

> "Is life a boon?
>   If so, it must befall
>   That Death, whene'er he call,
>   Must call too soon!"

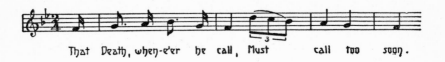

That Death, when-e'er he call, Must call too soon.

15

SPINACH, lettuce, cabbage, tomatoes, and fish—plenty of vegetables and no red meat—saved Gilbert's life. He threw away his medicines, traveled to the sunniest country he could think of, Egypt, and recovered from the crippling gout, rheumatism, and all the rest of his ills. He survived his partners, Sullivan and Carte, by many years.

Gilbert's last years were mellow and peaceful. On occasion he showed some of his old fiery spirit, but in the main he tried to be friendly and thoughtful. He was glad that he had had the generous impulse to write the friendly note to Sullivan just before the composer's death. It would have hurt Gilbert if his old friend and partner had died without being told that Gilbert was sorry for their quarrels and misunderstandings.

After Sullivan's death, Gilbert wrote only two librettos, neither of which brought him much glory. After *Fallen Fairies,* he announced that he would write nothing more for the comic opera theater. His last work was a short sketch, a piece of writing as grim as anything that ever horrified a theater audience. This was a play called *The Hooligan.* The old humorist had called the turn himself, when he wrote in *His Excellency,* a comic opera of 1892:

> "Though the notion you may scout,
>   I can prove beyond a doubt
> That the mine of jocularity is utterly worked out!"

The pride of his last years was the beautiful house he bought in Harrow Weald. It had been built by Norman Shaw for the Victorian painter Frederick Goodall. Gilbert altered the original name of Graeme's Dyke to Grim's Dyke, which some of his old enemies said was most appropriate.

In an article in the *World's Magazine,* Bram Stoker, of *Dracula* fame, wrote a description of this beautiful estate which remained Gilbert's home until his death:

"The house is large and has many large and handsome rooms, all of which are stored with objects of interest and beauty. The great drawing-room, formerly the painter's studio, which has the dimensions and windows of a chapel, is the storehouse of works of art. The fireplace, a massive carving in Cornish alabaster some fifteen feet high, was designed by Sir William himself . . .

"Scattered through the rooms are some lovely cabinets, one of great beauty. Italian of the XIVth century, another Japanese three hundred years old wrought in lacquer, tortoiseshell, cedar, ivory, and agate. On one table is a great ivory goblet German XVth century—on another table is an exquisite sculpture of a cat and kittens (Freminet, 1863).

"Elsewhere in the house, scattered among works of art and curios of all kinds, are interesting souvenirs of the dramatist's own plays. For instance, in the billiard-room is the block and axe so long used in *The Yeomen of the Guard.* Here too are 250 draw-

ings from the *Bab Ballads* framed. In the hall—wherein is a fine
suit of steel armor—is a huge model of a full-rigged ship. It rests
on a sea of green glass, and is fourteen feet long. It is a facsimile of
one of the old three-deckers of a hundred and ten guns sent to the
Black Sea at the Crimean War—the *Queen*, in which Sir Evelyn
Wood was a midshipman."

The extensive grounds of this old home were beautifully land-
scaped, with spacious lawns and well-kept gardens of flowers.
There was a veritable zoo on the place, too, where Gilbert kept
lemurs and other odd animals. There was poultry, and there were
rabbits, but it is doubtful if any of them reached the Gilbert table.
Gilbert, who has been accused of cruelty because of the strange
punishments and torments he devised for his ballads and plays,
admitted that he could never kill a black beetle, even. He confessed
that he ate meat, that he was quite willing for *others* to slaughter
what he required for his table; but he himself found something so
wonderful in the mechanism of life that he could not bring himself
to still it forever. To him it was like smashing a fine watch.

The Gilberts gave fancy-dress dinners, at which the playwright
delighted to appear as an Arab chief. They gave balls, and they
gave children's parties. Gilbert, with no children of his own, contented himself with loving other people's youngsters. There were
always a few children on the lawns at the garden parties at Grim's
Dyke, and Gilbert was never happier than when he was devising
games for twenty or thirty small guests.

Nothing illustrates Gilbert's new mellow mood better than the
fact that he agreed to become a member of the Garrick Club. Many
years before, he had been black-balled, through an error. Embar-
rassed members tried to explain, and wanted to put his name before
the club again. Gilbert would not hear of it. When at last he de-

cided to forgive them, he was the happiest one of all over the decision.

In 1907, the playwright was knighted. The honor which Victoria denied him was conferred by Edward VII. It was Gilbert's first impulse to turn it down, but, on second thought, he decided to accept it, since he would be the first playwright to be knighted for his work in the theater alone. He felt that it was his craft rather than himself receiving recognition.

Gilbert bought automobiles and had accidents with them. He once wrote a friend that he ran into a buggy and "spoiled a parson."

He became a local justice of the peace. It was quite like him to forget his own misadventures in motoring and hand out stiff sentences to others who had mishaps.

His friends hardly recognized Gilbert, he seemed so mild. Stories still circulated about his meeting with Reginald de Koven, for instance. The young American composer came to see the great English librettist, hoping to write some music for him. Gilbert looked the young man up and down for full five minutes without saying a word.

"You're very young!" said Gilbert finally.

"That, Mr. Gilbert," said de Koven furiously, "is something time will cure!"

Gilbert lost his chance to collaborate with the very talented composer of *Robin Hood*.

A hopeful composer from one of the Dominions wrote Gilbert to say that he would like to write an opera with him.

"I am a chemist by profession," he said, "but a born musician."

Gilbert wrote back, "I'd rather work with someone who is a born chemist, and a composer by profession!"

That was the Gilbert of the old days. In his Indian summer he was more likely to say, "I am a crumbling ruin—a magnificent ruin, no doubt, but still a ruin—and, like all ruins, I look best by moonlight."

He met death very gallantly. On May 29th, 1911, two young women had been invited to Grim's Dyke to learn to swim in the beautiful lagoon which Gilbert had built with his own hands. One of the girls got beyond her depth and called for help. Gilbert plunged in to save her, but the exertion and cold water were too much for a man in his seventies. He was dead before help could be called.

"I should like to die upon a summer day in my own garden," he had once remarked to a friend. And so he had.

Gilbert abhorred funeral processions and ceremonies. His last wishes were carried out faithfully by his widow. With the simplest of ceremonies, his funeral urn was placed in Great Stanmore churchyard.

Gilbert's memorial, on the Victoria Embankment, bears the terse inscription:

> "His foe was folly
> & his weapon wit."

That would have pleased Gilbert.

It was all over. The last of the Savoy partners was gone. They left the world a rich heritage of humor and wit and melody. The Savoy operas are the true memorials to Gilbert and Sullivan and Carte.

THE WORKS OF
GILBERT AND SULLIVAN IN COLLABORATION
The Savoy Operas

(The operas are listed in chronological order, with the names of the theaters where they were first produced, and the dates of the first-night performances.)

Thespis; or, The Gods Grown Old; Gaiety Theater, London; December 23, 1871 (See *Songs: Little Maid of Arcadee*).

Trial by Jury (Dramatic cantata); Royalty Theatre, Dean Street, Soho, London; March 25, 1875; vocal score with dialogue published by Chappell, 1875.

The Sorcerer; Opéra Comique, London; November 17, 1877; vocal score with piano accompaniment published by Metzler, 1877; revised edition, 1844.

H.M.S. Pinafore; or, The Lass That Loved a Sailor; Opéra Comique, London; May 25, 1878; vocal score with piano accompaniment published by Metzler, 1878.

The Pirates of Penzance; or, The Slave of Duty; Royal Bijou Theatre, Paignton, England, December 30, 1879 (Copyright performance); Fifth Avenue Theatre, New York, December 31, 1879 (U.S. premiere); Opéra Comique, London, April 3, 1880 (English premiere); vocal score with piano accompaniment published by Chappell, 1880.

Patience; or, Bunthorne's Bride; Opéra Comique, London; April 23, 1881; vocal score with piano accompaniment published by Chappell, 1881.

Iolanthe; or, The Peer and the Peri; Savoy Theatre, London; November 25, 1882; vocal score with piano accompaniment published by Chappell, 1883.

Princess Ida; or, Castle Adamant; Savoy Theatre, London; January 5, 1884; vocal score with piano accompaniment published by Chappell, 1884.

The Mikado; or, The Town of Titipu; Savoy Theatre, London; March 14, 1885; vocal score with piano accompaniment published by Chappell, 1885; full score published by Bosworth, 1900.

Ruddigore; or, The Witch's Curse; Savoy Theatre, London; January 22, 1887; vocal score with piano accompaniment published by Chappell, 1887.

The Yeomen of the Guard; or, The Merryman and His Maid; Savoy Theatre, London; October 3, 1888; vocal score with piano accompaniment published by Chappell, 1888.

The Gondoliers; or, The King of Barataria; Savoy Theatre, London; December 7, 1889; vocal score with piano accompaniment published by Chappell, 1890.

Utopia, Limited; or, The Flowers of Progress; Savoy Theatre, London; October 7, 1893; vocal score with piano accompaniment published by Chappell, 1893.

The Grand Duke; or, The Statutory Duel; Savoy Theatre, London; March 7, 1896; vocal score with piano accompaniment published by Chappell, 1896.

SEE ALSO *Martyr of Antioch, The:* WORKS OF ARTHUR SEYMOUR SULLIVAN, SACRED ORATORIOS AND CANTATAS.

THE WORKS OF WILLIAM SCHWENCK GILBERT *

Ages Ago, musical piece for the German Reed repertory; Fred Clay, composer; Gallery of Illustration, 1869.

Bab Ballads, illustrated by the author; editions published by John Camden Hotten, 1869; Routledge, 1870, 1873, 1876, 1877, 1878, 1882, 1887, 1889; Macmillan & Co., 1904.

Brantinghame Hall, drama; St. James's Theatre, November 27, 1888.

Brigands, The, English version of an opéra bouffe by Offenbach; published by Boosey, 1884.

Broken Hearts, a fairy play; Court Theatre, December 9, 1875; Lacey's Acting Edition of Plays, 1881.

Charity, melodrama; Haymarket Theatre, January 3, 1874; Lacey's Acting Edition of Plays, 1885.

Cock Robin, pantomime; Lyceum, 1867.

Comedy and Tragedy, drama; Lyceum, January 26, 1884; Lacey's Acting Edition of Plays.

Creatures of Impulse, a musical fairy tale; Court Theatre, April 15, 1871; Lacey's Acting Edition of Plays.

* This list includes the playwright's most successful and best-known works for the theater, as well as the titles of several collections of verse and short stories. Most of Gilbert's important plays appear in the four series of *Original Plays,* published by the English house of Chatto & Windus, 1876 and 1911. Other English publishers of the plays are listed with the titles above.

Dan'l Druce, Blacksmith, drama; Haymarket Theatre, September 11, 1876; Lacey's Acting Edition of Plays, 1881.

Dulcamara; or, The Little Duck and the Great Quack, a burlesque of *L'Elisire du' Amore;* St. James's Theatre, December 1866.

Engaged, farce; Haymarket Theatre, October 3, 1877; Lacey's Acting Edition of Plays, 1881.

Eyes and No Eyes, musical piece for the German Reed repertory; Florian Pascal, composer; Gallery of Illustration, 1875.

Fairy's Dilemma, The, a fantastic drama; Garrick Theatre, May 3, 1904.

Fallen Fairies, operetta based on Gilbert's *The Wicked World;* Edward German, composer; Savoy Theatre, September 16, 1909.

Foggerty's Fairy, a collection of short stories, 1869.

Foggerty's Fairy, a comedy; Criterion Theatre, December 1881.

Fortune Hunter, The, drama; Road Company production, Edinburgh, Scotland, 1898.

Gentleman in Black, The, a musical legend; Court Theatre, 1871; Lacey's Acting Edition of Plays, 1871.

Great Expectations, dramatization of Dickens's novel; Court Theatre, May 28, 1871.

Gretchen, verse drama; Olympic Theatre, March 24, 1879.

Happy Arcadia, musical piece for the German Reed repertory; Fred Clay, composer; Galley of Illustration, October 28, 1872.

Happy Land, The, burlesque version of Gilbert's *The Wicked World* in collaboration with Gilbert à Beckett; Court Theatre, 1873.

His Excellency, comic opera; Dr. Osmond Carr, composer; Lyric Theatre, October 27, 1894; published by Chappell, 1894.

Hooligan, The, drama, 1911.

Illustrations by William S. Gilbert for works of other authors: *An Algerian Monkey versus British Apes* (*The Spectre*), 1864; *Magic Mirror, The,* by William Gilbert, Sr., 1866; *King George's Middy,* by William Gilbert, Sr., 1869; *Fiend's Delight, The,* by "Dod Grile" (Ambrose Bierce), 1873; *London Characters,* by H. Mayhew, 1874.

Medical Man, A; published in the collection *Drawing-Room Plays and Parlour Pantomimes;* London, 1870.

Merry Zingara, The; or, The Pipsy-Wipsy and the Tipsy Gypsy, parody on Balfe's and Bunn's *The Bohemian Girl;* New Royalty Theatre, March 21, 1868.

Mountebanks, The, comic opera; Alfred Cellier, composer; Lyric Theatre, January 4, 1892; published by Chappell, 1892.

No Cards, a musical piece for the German Reed repertory; L. Elliot, composer; Gallery of Illustration, 1869; published by Williams, 1902.

Old Score, An, a comedy (Original title *Quits,* privately printed edition); Gaiety Theatre, July 19, 1869; Lacey's Acting Edition of Plays, 1870, 1876.

On Bail, farce, adapted from *Le Reveillon;* Lacey's Acting Edition of Plays, 1881.

On Guard, comedy; Court Theatre, October 28, 1871; Lacey's Acting Edition of Plays. 1874.

Ought We to Visit Her?, dramatized novel, 1875.

Our Island Home, musical piece for the German Reed repertory; Thomas German Reed, composer; Gallery of Illustration, June 20, 1870.

Palace of Truth, The, a fairy drama; The Haymarket Theatre, November 19, 1870; Lacey's Acting Edition of Plays, 1871.

Pretty Druidess, The; or, The Mother, the Maid and the Mistletoe Bough, a parody of *Norma;* New Royalty Theatre, 1869.

Princess, The, a whimsical allegory based on Tennyson's poem; Olympic Theatre, 1870; Lacey's Acting Edition of Plays, 1870, 1876.

Pygmalion and Galatea, a "mythological comedy"; Haymarket Theatre, December 9, 1871; Lacey's Acting Edition of Plays, 1875.

Quits, see *Old Score, An.*

Randall's Thumb, melodrama; Court Theatre, January 25, 1871; Lacey's Acting Edition of Plays, 1872.

Robert the Devil, an operatic extravaganza; Gaiety Theatre, December 21, 1868; published by Phillips, 1868.

Rosenkranz and Guildenstern, a travesty of Shakespeare's *Hamlet;* The Vaudeville, June 1891; Lacey's Acting Edition of Plays, 1893.

Ruy Blas, a burlesque, printed in *Warne's Christmas Annual,* 1866.

Sensation Novel, A, an operetta for the German Reed repertory; Florian Pascal, composer; Gallery of Illustration, 1871; published by Williams, 1912.

Sweethearts, dramatic comedy; Prince of Wales's Theatre, November 7, 1874; Lacey's Acting Edition of Plays, 1878.

Tom Cobb; or, Fortune's Toy, a farce; St. James's Theatre, April 24, 1875; Lacey's Acting Edition of Plays, 1880.

Topsy-Turveydom, farce, 1874.

Vivandiere, The; or, True to the Corps, operetta extravaganza; St. James's Hall, Liverpool, June 15, 1867; published by Montague, 1868.

Wedding March, The, an eccentricity; Court Theatre, November 15, 1873; Lacey's Acting Edition of Plays, 1879.

Wicked World, The, a fairy comedy, 1873; private printing, 1875; Lacey's Acting Edition of Plays, 1875, 1887.

THE WORKS OF ARTHUR SEYMOUR SULLIVAN

Ballets

L'Ille Enchantée; Covent Garden, May 14, 1864.

Victoria and Merrie England; Alhambra Theatre, May 25, 1897; piano arrangement by W. Bendall, Metzler, 1897.

Hymn Tunes

Audite Audientes Me (I Heard the Voice of Jesus Say); New Church Hymn Book, No. 408; Shaw, 1874.

Bolwell (Thou to Whom the Sick and Dying); Hymn Tunes, No. 45; Novello, 1902.

Carrow (My God, I Thank Thee); Congregational Psalmist, No. 496; Hodder & Stoughton, 1875.

Chapel Royal (O Love That Wilt Not Let Me Go); Hymn Tunes, No. 44; Novello, 1902.

Church Hymns with Tunes, edited by Arthur S. Sullivan, contains twenty-four original tunes: *Christus, Clarence, Coena Domini, Dulci Sonantia, Ever Faithful, Evelyn, Golden Sheaves, Hanford, Holy City, Hushed was the Evening Hymn, Lux Eoi, Lux in Tenebrae, Paradise, Pilgrimage, Resurrexit, St. Francis, St. Millicent, St. Patrick, St. Theresa, Saints of God, Ultor Omnipotens, Valete, Veni Creator.*

Constance; New Church Hymn Book, No. 511; Shaw, 1874.

Courage, Brother; Good Words, Strahan, 1872.

Dominion Hymn (God Bless Our Wide Dominion); Chappell, 1880.

Ecclesia (The Church Has Waited Long); New Church Hymn Book, No. 64; Shaw, 1874.

Formosa; Psalms and Hymns for Divine Worship, No. 273; Nisbet, 1867 and 1872.

Gennesareth; Sarum Hymnal, No, 288, 1869; *Hymnary,* Novello, 1872.

Hymnary, The, Sullivan's tunes in, Novello, 1872: *Angel Voices, Gentle Shepherd (The Long Home), Lacrymae, Lux Mundi, Onward, Christian Soldiers, Propior Deo, Safe Home, St. Edmund, St. Kevin, Saviour, When in Dust to Thee, Venite, Welcome, Happy Morning.*

Hymns for Children, words by Sarah Wilson; Eyre & Spottiswoode, 1888.

Hymn of the Homeland; Good Words, Strahan, 1867; Boosey, 1868.

Mount Zion; Psalms and Hymns for Divine Worship, No. 221; Nisbet, 1867, 1872.

Of Thy Love; Book of Praise Hymnal, No. 320; Macmillan, 1868.

O King of Kings (written by command for the Queen's Jubilee); Eyre & Spottiswoode, 1897.

Onward, Christian Soldiers; published in *Musical Times,* December 1871; see also *Hymnary, The.*

Promissio Patris (Our Blest Redeemer); New Church Hymn Book, No. 167; Shaw, 1874.

Roseate Hues, The; Parish Choir Book, No. 553; Novello, 1901.

St. Luke; Psalms and Hymns for Divine Worship, No. 285; Nisbet, 1867, 1872.

Son of God, The, an arrangement; *Brown Borthwick's Supplemental Hymn and Tune Book,* Third Edition, No. 74; Novello, 1869.

Strain Upraise, The; Brown Borthwick's Supplemental Hymn and Tune Book,
Third Edition, No. 68; Novello, 1869.

Thou God of Love; Book of Praise Hymnal, No. 306; Macmillan, 1868.

Upon the Snow-Clad Earth, carol; Metzler, 1876.

Victoria (To Mourn Our Dead We Gather Here); Hymn Tunes, No. 33; Novello, 1902.

Incidental Music

The Foresters (Tennyson); Daly's Theater, New York, March 25, 1892; vocal
score with piano accompaniment published by Chappell, 1892.

Henry VIII (Shakespeare); Theatre Royal, Manchester, England, August 29, 1877;
piano arrangement, Metzler, 1879.

King Arthur (J. Comyns Carr); Lyceum Theatre, January 12, 1895; arrangement
for concert performance by W. Bendall published by Novello, 1903; string
parts, Novello, 1904.

Macbeth (Shakespeare); Lyceum Theatre, December 29, 1888; overture published
by Chappell, 1888; full score, Chappell, 1893.

Merchant of Venice, The (Shakespeare); Prince's Theatre, Manchester, England,
September 19, 1871; piano duet published by Cramer, 1873; piano solo by
J. Rummel, published by Cramer, 1877; full score and piano arrangement,
Bosworth, Leipzig, 1878.

Merry Wives of Windsor, The (Shakespeare); Gaiety Theatre, December 19, 1874.

Tempest, The (Shakespeare); played in Leipzig, April 11, 1861, at the Gewandhaus; re-scored and performed at Crystal Palace, London, April 5, 1862; full
score, Cramer, 1864; vocal score, chorus parts, Novello, 1875; Franklin Taylor's arrangement, Novello, 1891.

Masques, Cantatas, Patriotic Odes

Exhibition Ode, written for the opening of the Colonial and Indian Exhibition,
1886; Albert Hall, May 4, 1886; vocal score published by Novello, 1886.

Golden Legend, The (Longfellow); cantata arranged by J. Bennett; Leeds Festival, October 16, 1886; vocal score published by Novello, 1886; full score,
Novello, 1887.

Imperial Institute Ode, written and composed for the occasion of laying the
foundation stone of the Imperial Institute, July 4, 1887; Lewis Morris, poet;
vocal score published by Chappell, 1887.

Kenilworth, masque; H. J. Chorley, librettist; Birmingham Festival, September
8, 1864; vocal score published by Chappell, 1865.

On Shore and Sea, cantata; Tom Taylor, librettist; produced at the opening of
the International Exhibition, Albert Hall, May 1, 1871; vocal score published
by Boosey, 1871; see also *Part Songs: Song of Peace.*

Operas and Operettas

(This list does not include the Savoy Operas, written in collaboration with Gilbert.)

Beauty Stone, The, romantic musical drama; A. W. Pinero and Comyns Carr, librettists; Savoy Theatre, May 28, 1898; vocal score with piano accompaniment, Chappell, 1898.

Chieftain, The (enlarged version of *The Contrabandista*), comic opera; F. C. Burnand, librettist; Savoy Theatre, December 12, 1894; vocal score with piano accompaniment, Boosey, 1895.

Contrabandista, The, comic opera; F. C. Burnand, librettist; St. George's Hall, December 18, 1867; vocal score with piano accompaniment, Boosey, 1871; see also: *Chieftain, The.*

Cox and Box, comic operetta; libretto by F. C. Burnand, based on *Box and Cox,* a farce by Maddison Morton; privately produced, London, April 27, 1867; vocal score with dialogue, Boosey, 1871.

Emerald Isle, The, comic opera, completed by Edward German; Basil Hood, librettist; Savoy Theatre, April 27, 1901; vocal score with piano accompaniment, Chappell, 1901.

Haddon Hall, light opera; Sydney Grundy, librettist; Savoy Theatre, September 24, 1892; vocal score with piano accompaniment, Chappell, 1892.

Ivanhoe, romantic opera (Sir Walter Scott's *Ivanhoe*); J. Sturgis, librettist; Royal English Opera House, January 31, 1891; vocal score with piano accompaniment, Chappell, 1891; full score, Chappell, 1891.

Rose of Persia, The, comic opera; Basil Hood, librettist; Savoy Theatre, November 29, 1899; vocal score with piano accompaniment, Chappell, 1900; full score, Bosworth, Leipzig, 1901.

Sapphire Necklace, an unfinished opera, 1863–4; H. J. Chorley, librettist; overture played at St. James's Hall, July 11, 1866. Two numbers published: *Over the Roof,* song, Cramer, 1866, 1885; *When Love and Beauty,* madrigal, Novello, 1898.

Zoo, The, comic opera; B. C. Stephenson, librettist; St. James's Theatre, June 5, 1875.

Orchestral Works

Additional accompaniments to Handel's *Jephthah,* 1869.

Cadenza to Mozart's *Concerto in A,* 1859; performed at Leipzig.

Choral and Orchestral Fugue, "Cum Sancto Spiritu," 1857.

Concerto for Violoncello, 1866; played by Piatti at Crystal Palace, November 24, 1866.

Di Ballo Overture, 1870; Birmingham Festival, August 31, 1870; full score published by Stanley Lucas, Weber & Co., 1882; piano duet by A. O'Leary, Novello, 1909.

Imperial March, composed for the opening of the Imperial Institute, 1893; orchestral and military band parts, Chappell, 1893.

In Memorium Overture, Norwich Festival, October 30, 1866; full score, arrangements for piano solo and piano duet, Novello, 1885.

Marmion, Philharmonic Society, London, June 3, 1867.

Overture, "Feast of Roses," 1859.

Overture in C Minor, "Timon of Athens," 1857.

Overture in D Minor, 1858.

Princess of Wales' March; arrangements for piano solo and piano duet, Cramer, 1863.

Procession March; arrangements for piano solo and piano duet, Cramer, 1863.

Psalm for Chorus and Orchestra, 1858.

Sapphire Necklace Overture, see *Sapphire Necklace*, an unfinished opera.

Symphony in E (Irish Symphony); Crystal Palace, March 10, 1866; full score, Novello, 1915.

Part Songs

Beleaguered, The; Novello, 1868.

Coming Home (duet); Boosey, 1873.

Echoes, No. 6 of *Six Four-Part Songs* (also published separately); Novello, 1868.

Evening, No. 3 of *Six Four-Part Songs* (also published separately); Novello, 1868.

Fair Daffodills (four-part song); Novello, 1903.

I Sing the Birth (Sacred part song); Boosey, 1868.

It Came Upon the Midnight (Sacred part song); Boosey, 1871.

Joy to the Victors, No. 4 of *Six Four-Part Songs* (also published separately); Novello, 1868.

The Last Night of the Year (four-part song); Novello, 1863, 1864.

Lead, Kindly Light (Sacred part song); Boosey, 1871.

The Long Day Closes; Novello, 1868.

Morn, Happy Morn (trio), in the play *Olivia;* Metzler, 1878.

O Hush Thee, My Babie, No. 2 of *Six Four-Part Songs;* Novello, 1867, 1868.

Parting Gleams, No. 5 of *Six Four-Part Songs* (also published separately); Novello, 1868.

Rainy Day, The, No. 1 of *Six Four-Part Songs;* Novello, 1867, 1868.

Seaside Thoughts (four-part song for men's voices), 1857; Novello, 1904.

Sisters, The (duet), published in the *Leisure Hour;* Stanley Lucas, Weber & Co., 1881.

Song of Peace, part song from the cantata *On Shore and Sea;* Boosey, 1868.

Through Sorrow's Path (sacred part song); Boosey, 1871.

Watchman, What of the Night? (sacred part song); Boosey, 1871.

Way is Long and Drear, The (sacred part song); Boosey, 1871.

When Love and Beauty (madrigal), 1863; Novello, 1898; see *Sapphire Necklace, The,* an unfinished opera.

Piano Compositions

Day Dreams, six pieces for piano solo; Boosey, 1867; German edition: Kistner, Leipzig.

Duo Concertante, for Violoncello and Pianoforte; Lamborn Cock, Addison & Co., 1868.

Marche Danoise, piano solo; Weippert & Co., 1871; Stanley Lucas, Weber & Co., 1874.

Sonata for Piano, 1857.

Thoughts, two pieces for piano solo, 1862; No. 1—Allegretto con grazia; No. 2—Allegro grazioso.

Twilight, piano solo; Chappell, 1868; German edition: Kistner, Leipzig.

Sacred Oratorios and Cantatas

Light of the World, The, oratorio; Birmingham Festival, August 27, 1873; vocal score, Cramer, 1873.

Prodigal Son, The, oratorio; Worcester Festival, September 8, 1869; vocal score, Boosey, 1869.

Martyr of Antioch, The, sacred music drama; poem by Dean Millman; libretto by William S. Gilbert; Leeds Music Festival, October 15, 1880; vocal score, Chappell, 1880, 1898; full score, Chappell, 1899.

Services, Anthems, and Carols

All this Night, carol; Novello, 1870.

Festival Te Deum, in celebration of the recovery of the Prince of Wales, Crystal Palace, May 1, 1872; vocal score, Novello, 1872; full score, Novello, 1887.

Hark! What mean those Holy Voices?, 1883.

Hearken unto Me, anthem; Novello, 1877.

I Will Lay Me Down In Peace; Novello, 1910.

I Will Mention, anthem; Novello, 1875.

I Will Sing of Thy Power, anthem; Novello, 1877.

I Will Worship, anthem; Boosey, 1871.

Mercy and Truth, chorus adapted from Russian church music; Novello, 1874, 1899.

O God, Thou Art Worthy, anthem, 1867; Novello, 1871.

O Love the Lord, anthem; Novello, 1864.

O Taste and See, anthem; Novello, 1867.

Rejoice in the Lord, anthem; Boosey, 1868.

Sing, O Heavens, anthem; Boosey, 1869.

Sing Unto the Lord and Praise His Name, anthem; sung in 1855 in the Chapel Royal during Sullivan's choristership.

Te Deum, Jubilate and Kyrie, in D, service; Novello, 1866 and 1872.

Te Deum Laudamus, a Thanksgiving for Victory (Boer War), 1900; performed at St. Paul's, June 8, 1902, at the close of the South African War; full score and vocal score, Novello, 1902.

There is None Like Unto the God of Jeshurun, anthem; composed by Sir John Goss, completed by Arthur S. Sullivan; Novello, 1882.

Turn Thee Again, chorus adapted from Russian church music; Novello, 1874, 1899.

Turn Thy Face, anthem; Novello, 1878.

Upon the Snowclad Earth, carol; Metzler, 1876.

We have heard with our ears, anthem; Novello, 1865.

Who is Like Unto Thee?, anthem; Novello, 1883.

Wreaths for our Graves, anthem; Novello, 1897, 1898.

Songs

Absent-Minded Beggar, The, 1899.

A Life that Lives for You; Boosey, 1870.

Arabian Love Song; Chappell, 1866.

A Weary Lot is Thine; Chappell, 1866.

Ay de mi, No. 2 of *The Young Mother;* Cramer, 1873; Metzler, 1876.

Bid me at Least Good-bye!, from the play *An Old Jew,* by Sydney Grundy; Chappell, 1894.

Birds in the Night, song from *Cox and Box* with different words; Boosey, 1869.

Bride from the North; Cramer, 1863.

Care is all fiddle-de-dee; see: *Miller and his Man, The.*

Chorister, The; see: *Young Mother, The.*

Christmas Bells at Sea; Novello, 1875.

County Guy; Ashdown, 1867.

Days are Cold, The (cradle song), No. 1 of *The Young Mother;* published by Metzler, 1876, as *Little Darling, Sleep Again.*

Distant Shore, The; Chappell, 1874.

Dove Song; Boosey, 1869.

Edward Gray; Stanley Lucas, Weber & Co., 1880.

Ever; Chappell, 1887.

First Departure, The, No. 3 of *The Young Mother;* Cramer, 1873; published by Metzler, 1878, as *The Chorister.*

Five Songs, words from Shakespeare, 1863–4; Metzler, 1866: *O Mistress Mine, Orpheus with his Lute, Rosalind, Sigh no more, Ladies, The Willow Song.*

Give; Boosey, 1867.

Golden Days; Boosey, 1872.

Guinevere; Cramer, 1872.

If Doughty Deeds; Chappell, 1866.

I heard the Nightingale; Chappell, 1863.

In the Summers Long Ago; published by Metzler, 1867, as *My Love Beyond the Sea.*

In the Twilight of our Love, from *Patience,* with different words; Chappell, 1881.

It was a Lover and his Lass, duet and chorus, 1857; performed at Royal Academy, July 14, 1857.

I Wish to Tune My Quiv'ring Lyre; Boosey, 1868.

I Would I Were a King; Boosey, 1878.

King Henry's Song, from *Henry VIII.* Incidental Music; Metzler, 1878.

Let me Dream Again; Boosey, 1875.

Living Poems; Boosey, 1874.

Little Darling, Sleep Again; see: *Young Mother, The.*

Longing for Home; Novello, 1904.

Looking Forward; Boosey, 1873.

Looking Back; Boosey, 1870.

Lost Chord, The; Boosey, 1877.

Love Laid his Sleepless Head, words by Swinburne, sung in the Gaiety production of *The Merry Wives of Windsor,* December 19, 1874; Boosey, 1875.

The Love that Loves me not; Novello, 1875.

Maid of Arcadee, from *Thespis;* Cramer, 1872.

Maiden's Story, The; Chappell, 1867.

Marquis de Mincepie, The; see: *Miller and his Man, The.*

Mary Morrison; Boosey, 1874.

Miller and his Man, The, drawing-room extravaganza written by F. C. Burnand, incidental music by F. Simpson, songs by Arthur S. Sullivan; songs: *Marquis de Mincepie, The, Care is all fiddle-de-dee;* vocal score with libretto, Cramer, 1874; separate edition of Sullivan's songs, Cramer, 1874.

Moon in Silent Brightness, The; Metzler, 1868.

Mother's Dream, The; Boosey, 1868.

My Child and I; Boosey, 1901.

My Dear and only Love; Boosey, 1874.

My Dearest Heart; Boosey, 1876.

My Heart Is Like a Silent Lute; Novello, 1904.

Nel Ciel Seren, serenata from the music to *The Merchant of Venice;* words by F. Rizzelli. (Also known as *Venetian Serenade*); Cramer, 1873.

None But I Can Say; Boosey, 1872.

O! Bella Mia; see: *Oh! Ma Charmante.*

O Fair Dove, O Fond Dove; Ashdown, 1868.

Old Love Letters; Boosey, 1879.

O Israel; Novello, 1855.

Oh! Ma Charmante, romance, Cramer, 1872; Italian version. *O! Bella Mia,* Cramer, 1873; English version: *Sweet Dreamer,* Cramer, 1874.

Once Again; Boosey, 1872.

O Swallow, Swallow; J. Church Co., 1900.

O Sweet and Fair; Boosey, 1868.

Over the Roof, from *The Sapphire Necklace;* Cramer, 1885.

River, The; Routledge, 1875; Novello, 1875.

Sad Memories; Metzler, 1869.

Sailor's Grave, The; Cramer, 1872.

St. Agnes' Eve; Boosey, 1879.

Shadow, A; Patey & Willis, 1886.

She is not Fair to Outward View; Boosey, 1866.

Sleep, my Love, Sleep; Boosey, 1874.

Snow Lies White, The; Boosey, 1868.

Sometimes; Boosey, 1877.

Sweet Day, so cool; Metzler, 1864; Ashdown & Parry, 1881.

Sweet Dreamer; see: *Oh! Ma Charmante.*

Sweethearts; Chappell, 1875.

Tears, Idle Tears; J. Church Co., 1900.

Tender and True; Chappell, 1874.

There Sits a Bird; Cramer, 1873.

Thou art Lost to Me; Boosey, 1865.

Thou'rt Passing Hence; Chappell, 1875.

Thou art Weary; Chappell, 1874.

To One in Paradise; Novello, 1904.

Troubador, The; Boosey, 1869.

Venetian Serenade; see: *Nel Ciel Seren.*

Village Chimes, The; Boosey, 1870.

We've Ploughed Our Land; Routledge, 1875; Novello, 1875.

What Does Little Birdie Say?; Ashdown, 1867.

When Thou art Near; Boosey, 1877.

White Plume, The; Weippert, 1872.

Will He Come?; Boosey, 1865.

Window, The; or, *The Songs of the Wrens,* a cycle of twelve songs, words by Tennyson; Strahan, 1871.

Young Mother, The, three songs, 1873. No. 1: Cradle Song—*The Days are Cold,* also called *Little Darling, Sleep Again;* No. 2: *Ay de mi;* No. 3: *The First Departure,* also called *The Chorister;* Cramer, 1874; Metzler, 1876.

You Sleep, in the play *The Profligate;* Chappell, 1889.

String Ensemble

Romance for String Quartet, 1859.

A LIST OF THE BEST BOOKS AND ARTICLES ON GILBERT AND SULLIVAN AND THEIR WORKS

The Story of Gilbert and Sullivan; or, The 'Compleat' Savoyard, by Isaac Goldberg, New York, Crown Publishers, 1935

Gilbert and Sullivan, by Hesketh Pearson, New York and London, Harper & Brothers Publishers, 1935

Gilbert and Sullivan, by A. H. Godwin, with an introduction by G. K. Chesterton, New York, E. P. Dutton & Co., London and Toronto, J. M. Dent & Sons Ltd.

W. S. Gilbert, His Life and Letters, by Sidney Dark and Rowland Grey, New York, George H. Doran Company, London, Methuen & Co. Ltd.

William Schwenck Gilbert, an autobiography in *The Theatre,* April 1883

W. S. Gilbert, by Edith A. Browne, London and New York, John Lane, 1907

Sir Arthur Sullivan, His Life, Letters & Diaries, by Herbert Sullivan and Newman Flower, with an introduction by Arnold Bennett, New York, George H. Doran Company, 1927

Sir Arthur Sullivan, Life Story, Letters and Reminiscences, by Arthur Lawrence, with critique by B. W. Findon and bibliography by Wilfred Bendall, Chicago and New York, Herbert S. Stone and Company, 1900

Arthur Seymour Sullivan, by Henry Saxe Wyndham, New York and London, Harper & Brothers, 1926

Gilbert & Sullivan, Opera, A History and a Comment, by H. M. Walbrook, London, F. V. White & Co. Ltd., 1922

Sullivan's Comic Operas, A Critical Appreciation, by Thomas F. Dunhill, London, Edward Arnold & Co., 1928 and 1929

The Last Pirate: Tales from the Gilbert and Sullivan Operas, by Louis Untermeyer, New York, Harcourt, Brace and Co., 1934

The Pinafore Picture Book, The Story of H.M.S. Pinafore, told by W. S. Gilbert, illustrated by Alice B. Woodward, New York, The Macmillan Company, 1908

The Story of The Mikado, told by W. S. Gilbert, illustrated by Alice B. Woodward, New York, Alfred A. Knopf

The Yeomen of the Guard, by W. S. Gilbert, London, Macmillan & Co. Ltd., 1929 (Libretto and illustrations)

Gilbert and Sullivan, A Romantic Prose Version of the Famous Operas, by Lillian Bradstock, London, Cecil Palmer, 1928

The Complete Plays of Gilbert and Sullivan, Garden City, New York, Garden City Publishing Co., Inc., 1941

Gilbert and Sullivan's H.M.S. Pinafore, adapted by Robert Lawrence, illustrated by Sheilah Beckett, New York, Grosset & Dunlap, 1940

Gilbert and Sullivan's The Mikado, adapted by Robert Lawrence, illustrated by Sheilah Beckett, New York, Grosset & Dunlap, 1940

Gilbert and Sullivan's The Gondoliers, adapted by Robert Lawrence, illustrated by Sheilah Beckett, New York, Grosset & Dunlap, 1940

Songs of a Savoyard, London, Routledge, 1890

Plays & Poems of W. S. Gilbert, with a preface by Deems Taylor, New York, Random House, 1932

A Treasury of Gilbert & Sullivan, edited by Deems Taylor, with arrangements of one hundred and two songs, by Dr. Albert Sirmay, New York, Simon and Schuster, 1941

Everybody's Favorite Gilbert and Sullivan Album, edited by E. M. Schumann, New York, Amsco Music Sales Co., 1938

A Gilbert and Sullivan Dictionary, by George E. Dunn, New York, Oxford University Press, 1936

Let's Do Some Gilbert & Sullivan, A Practical Handbook, by Edmond W. Rickett and Benjamin T. Hoogland, New York, Coward-McCann, Inc., 1940

How to Present the Gilbert and Sullivan Operas, by Albert D. Bassuk, with foreword by Dr. Sigmund Spaeth, New York, The Bass Publishers, 1934

The Gilbert and Sullivan Journal, published monthly since 1925 by The Gilbert and Sullivan Society, London

The Great Partnership, by Grant Overton in *The Mentor,* February 1928

The Story of "The Lost Chord," in *The Mentor,* February 1928

INDEX

267